£1·55

Scientific Greenhouse Gardening

Scientific Greenhouse Gardening

Peter Kincaid Willmott
MBE, NDH, FIBiol, AInstPRA

EP PUBLISHING LIMITED

Text and illustrations copyright © EP Publishing Limited 1982

ISBN 0 7158 0663 7

First edition 1982

Published by EP Publishing Limited, Bradford Road, East Ardsley, Wakefield, West Yorkshire, WF3 2JN, England

Printed and bound in Great Britain by Butler & Tanner Ltd, Frome, Somerset

Design: Krystyna Hewitt

Illustrations: Tony Gardiner

Photographs
ADAS, Ministry of Agriculture, Fisheries and Food/Crown copyright: pp. 29, 30, 119, 120
Brian Furner: pp. 88, 90, 94, 156
Halls Homes and Gardens Ltd., Tonbridge: p. 25
Douglas Hewitt: cover
ICI Ltd., Plant Protection Division: pp. 57, 58, 61
Pershore College of Horticulture: pp. 189, 190
P. K. Willmott: pp. 7, 8

All other photographs: Philip Gardner/EP Publishing Ltd.

Contents

Acknowledgements

I am grateful to my former colleagues at the Askham Bryan College of Agriculture and Horticulture and elsewhere for their willing and ready co-operation in enabling me to arrange the taking of photographs to illustrate this book.

I am also grateful to my various colleagues in horticultural education throughout the country who have shared their knowledge with me so readily and so freely over the years. They have helped me to bring together my views of the subject which I have tried to express in this book. Their objectivity and eagerness to establish scientific truth has been a most stimulating experience.

I am greatly obligated to Diana Uttley who so willingly and enthusiastically typed all my manuscripts. No one else could have transcribed my scrawl so patiently and so effectively as she did.

P. K. Willmott
May 1982

General

Chapter 1

Introduction

Greenhouses became an essential part of the garden from the latter part of the eighteenth century onwards. Such structures had long been in the minds of gardeners but their development had had to await the invention and production of cheap sheet glass. This in its turn had to wait upon the industrial revolution and the development of the necessary techniques.

Readers of Jane Austen's *Northanger Abbey* will recall General Tilney, with great pride, showing young Catherine Moreland his greenhouses. Jane Austen was writing this novel in about 1800, clearly showing that in the gardens of the great houses of that time greenhouses were well established. By the middle of the last century they were very much a status symbol among the gentry, and there was competition to see who could own the biggest. The prize probably went to the Duke of Devonshire whose head gardener, Joseph Paxton, built the famous glasshouse at Chatsworth, a project of such success that he went on to design and supervise the erection of the Crystal Palace in Hyde Park for the Great Exhibition of 1851.

The designs worked out in the early days changed little until the 1950s. Houses, some 8.5–9 m (*28–30 ft*) wide with eaves at 1.5 m (*5 ft*) and a span roof with a ridge at 4.0–4.3 m (*13 or 14 ft*), were developed for growing vines, and were later found equally suitable for tomatoes. Half a vinery was often erected against a wall to form a lean-to house, very popular against the walls of kitchen gardens. Smaller houses, some 4–4.3 m (*13 or 14 ft*) wide and 2.5–3 m (*8 or 9 ft*) to the ridge, also proved extremely useful for a whole variety of purposes. Market gardeners found them especially useful for cucumbers, and although commercial gardeners had used them before that time for producing pot plants of the kind favoured by the Victorians, they became known as cucumber houses. Greenhouses with very low walls were sometimes constructed over excavations and were

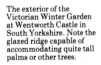

The exterior of the Victorian Winter Garden at Wentworth Castle in South Yorkshire. Note the glazed ridge capable of accommodating quite tall palms or other trees.

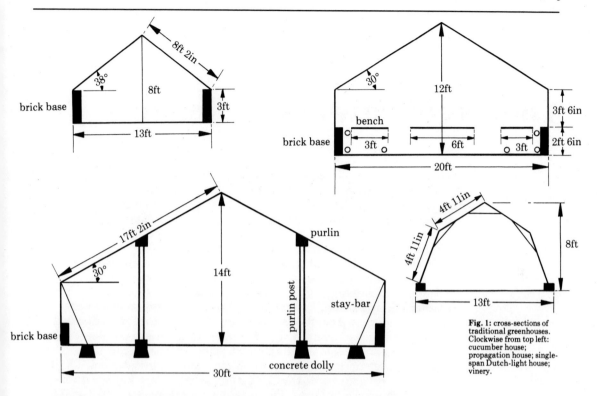

Fig. 1: cross-sections of traditional greenhouses. Clockwise from top left: cucumber house; propagation house; single-span Dutch-light house; vinery.

known as pits. This clumsy arrangement, now extinct, was largely a method of trying to conserve heat before central heating had been invented by a later generation of greenhouse growers. Another totally obsolete idea was that of a glass frame of sufficient size leaned against a wall to forward the growth of a peach or nectarine trained underneath. This was a peach case, which featured quite often in garden literature written before the Second World War.

Once reliable heating systems were available, the conservatory became a necessary addition to the gentleman's garden. Here were displayed flowering plants which a host could show off to his guests throughout the year. Most grand of all was the Winter Garden, a greenhouse of very generous proportions where a whole variety of temperate plants could be permanently planted safe from the frost. Sometimes it adjoined the dwelling itself so a stroll in a tiny simulated Mediterranean world was a pleasant alternative to one in the garden outside when the weather was too cold.

The age of the great garden has probably gone for ever, and with it its variety of glasshouses. The pineapple pit, the stove (an early name for a tropical house), the orchid house, the cool vinery, the heated vinery, the peach case, the conservatory and all the rest have passed into history. But the fascination of growing plants under glass remains, and is being enjoyed by amateur gardeners all over the country more and more.

So popular has the small greenhouse become, and so eager for knowledge its owner, that an attempt is made in the following pages to explain as straightforwardly as possible the management of a small greenhouse and the methods of growing the widest possible range of plants, both edible and decorative.

Chapter 2

The greenhouse microclimate

When a greenhouse is constructed, the space inside constitutes a special environment possessing its own miniature climate, known as the greenhouse microclimate. The properties of this microclimate are somewhat different from those of the general climate outside.

Temperature and humidity

The first of these differences is that the temperature within the greenhouse is always higher than that of the air outside. When the sun is shining brightly the difference may be very great indeed, but on clear winter nights it can be as little as 2 or 3 C° (centigrade degrees) $(3–5 F°)$, still a little warmer. The explanation for this is that heat enters the greenhouse by means of radiation from the sun and leaves it by means of radiation from the ground which it covers. The radiant heat from the sun is of short wavelengths and passes readily through glass, while that from the earth is of longer wavelengths and passes much less readily through glass. There is, therefore, a net gain due to the fact that glass behaves rather like a non-return valve for radiant heat. This is called the 'greenhouse effect' and is a well-known phenomenon in buildings with large windows and in closed motor cars. The need to remove excess heat from greenhouses during periods of bright sunshine led, at a very early stage in their development, to the inclusion of ventilators in their construction.

An obvious difference between the greenhouse microclimate and the general climate is that no rain falls on the soil it covers. If this soil is used for growing plants serious consequences can arise if it is not irrigated by approximately the same amount of water it would have received naturally as rain.

The relative humidity of the air within the greenhouse is usually higher than outside it and this, coupled with its stillness when the vents are closed, provides conditions very favourable for the germination and rapid development of the spores of the fungi causing mildews and rots. Exerting some control over relative humidity (R.H.) is yet another task forced upon the gardener if he is to manage his greenhouse successfully.

Light transmission

Another way in which the microclimate is different is in respect of light. By no means all of the light coming from the sun is able to penetrate into the greenhouse, and so it is always darker within the house than outside it. In summer, provided it is not shaded by trees or buildings, there is light in abundance and sufficient enters the house to provide for all the needs of the plants.

During the winter there is insufficient natural light for plants to grow in the open, let alone under glass, so it is obvious that everything possible must be done to allow the maximum amount of light to enter the greenhouse.

It would be quite simple, albeit expensive, to provide sufficient heat within a greenhouse during the winter months to make it warm enough for tomatoes, but while they might survive they would certainly not grow satisfactorily, neither would they set and provide ripened fruit. This would be entirely due to insufficient light energy reaching their leaves to enable them to photosynthesise, the process by which plants manufacture sugars and starches which they use for growth and energy production.

If a greenhouse is to be used only from mid-April to mid-October the light problem is greatly reduced. But if it is heated and to be used in the winter months the problem is acute. There are five factors which control light transmission into the house: the shade cast by buildings and trees; the shade cast by opaque parts of the greenhouse such as glazing bars; the design of the house; its orientation; and last but by no means least, the cleanness of the glass.

It is a matter of common sense that the greenhouse should have an unobstructed view of the southern sky and also the southern halves of the eastern and western ones. While this may be common sense, it may be

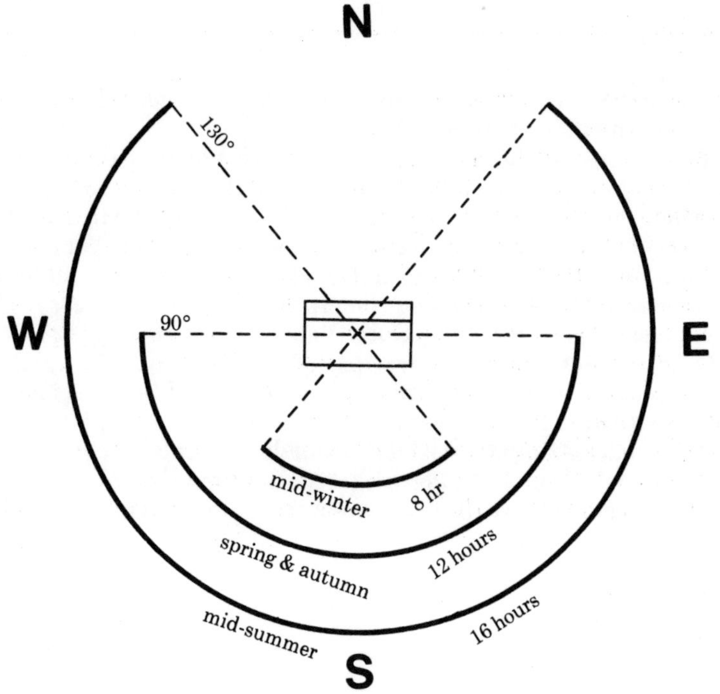

Fig. 2: the traverse of the sun relative to the southern horizon throughout the year. (After Lawrence, 1948.)

almost impossible to achieve in some gardens. Hedges, trees, fences and neighbouring houses cannot be removed and may affect the decision whether or not to have a greenhouse, or at least whether to heat it. For eight weeks either side of Christmas the mean height of the sun above the horizon is about 12 degrees at 52° latitude (southern England). Before buying a greenhouse, then, stand where you intend to put it and take a look to the south, trying to estimate what angle of elevation you need to get a clear view of the sky. If it exceeds 12 degrees most of the winter sunshine will be lost, and heating in winter would be a doubtful proposition. If it exceeds 25 degrees all the winter sunshine will be lost and unless you intend to grow ferns or other shade-tolerant plants heating would be folly. If it exceeds about 40 degrees the greenhouse will be at a permanent

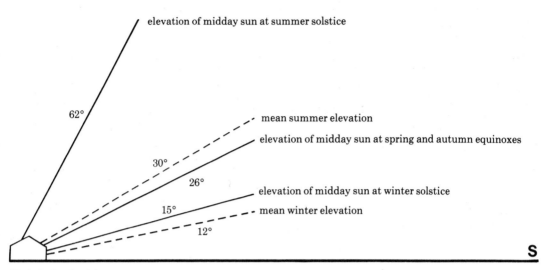

elevation of midday sun at summer solstice

62°

mean summer elevation

elevation of midday sun at spring and autumn equinoxes

30°

26°

elevation of midday sun at winter solstice

15°

mean winter elevation

12°

S

Fig. 3: the elevation of the sun in the four seasons (latitude 52°).

disadvantage even in midsummer, and not really worthwhile if frustration and disappointment are to be avoided.

The shadows cast by the opaque parts of the greenhouse structure cannot be avoided, but a considerable amount of effort has gone into designs which reduce them to the minimum. It all boils down to using the largest sheet of glass together with the smallest size of glazing bar and other structural parts consistent with strength and safety. The smallest sheet of glass acceptable today is one measuring 600 × 600 mm (*2 ft × 2 ft*). Best is the sheet of glass used for a Dutch light which measures 1423 × 731 mm (*56 × 28¾ in*), but unless this is supported on all four sides by a glazing bar, the glass needs to be of very heavy gauge. This combination of large size of glass with a small size of bar is now achieved by building the house with metal, using glazing strips which are made of aluminium alloy (which never requires painting). If the house exceeds a certain size the most successful arrangement is to have a framework of zinc-galvanised steel

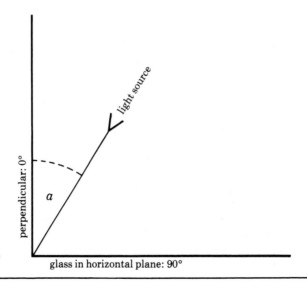

perpendicular: 0°

light source

a

Fig. 4; the angle of incidence (*a*) of a light-ray on a sheet of glass.

glass in horizontal plane: 90°

with aluminium-alloy cladding. Few garden greenhouses, however, exceed the size where they cannot be made entirely of glass and aluminium alloy.

The design, insofar as its shape is concerned, has a direct bearing upon light transmission because it determines the angle at which rays of light from the sun strike the glass. This angle is known as the angle of incidence (see Fig. 4) and it can vary from 0° to 90°. If the light strikes the glass at 0°, that is to say perpendicularly, then 90 per cent of it will pass through the glass. There is no appreciable loss of light transmission until the angle of incidence exceeds 40° after which it drops very rapidly to a point where

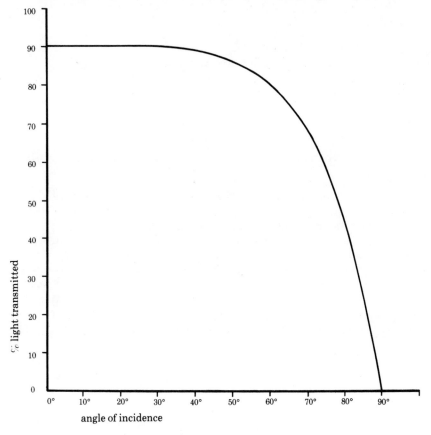

Fig. 5: the percentage of light transmitted through a pane of glass as a function of the angle of incidence. Most of the light not transmitted is reflected off. (After Lawrence, 1948.)

more light is reflected back than passes through (see Fig. 5). The importance of having the smallest possible angle of incidence between glass and sunbeam is easy enough to understand, but it must be considered along with the fourth factor, which is the orientation of the greenhouse.

Orientation

Traditionally greenhouses were orientated north–south on the correct assumption that each side of the greenhouse would receive an equal amount of sunshine during the course of a day provided that the weather stayed more or less the same. Unfortunately it means that in the winter each side gets a more or less equal share of very little. This is because the mean angle of incidence will be 78°, when less than 50 per cent of the incident (direct) light will get through the glass. Things are much worse than this, however, because the lower the angle of the sun the greater is the

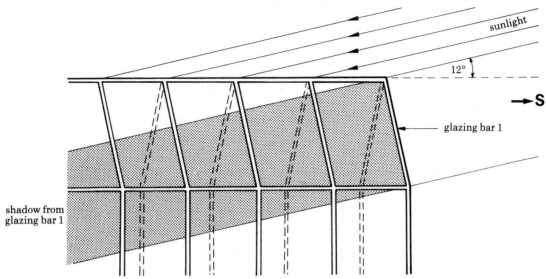

Fig. 6: the shadow cast by wooden glazing bars in winter in a house oriented north-south. The lower the elevation of the sun, the greater the shade.
The shading effect can be greatly reduced by orienting the house east-west, or by using smaller aluminium glazing bars.

shadow cast by the glazing bars (see Fig 6).

Our attention was first drawn to these facts by one of this century's greatest gardeners, Mr W. J. C. Lawrence, when he was the Head of the Garden Department at the John Innes Horticultural Institution at Merton, England. (Incidentally he, with his colleague J. C. Newall, devised the John Innes Composts; see page 32.) Lawrence became convinced that it was far more sensible to orientate greenhouses east-west. He was able to show that a greenhouse so orientated transmitted at least 27 per cent more of the winter light. He was by no means satisfied with this and went on to prove that by having a greenhouse with an uneven span (see Fig. 7) the light transmission could be increased by 63 per cent. In spite of

Fig. 7: this uneven-span greenhouse allows the best transmission of winter sunlight, but is much more expensive than houses of conventional design.

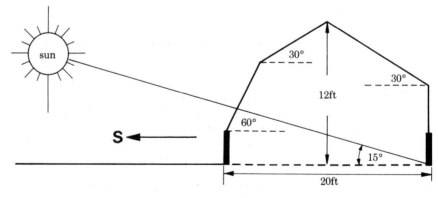

his great enthusiasm the uneven span houses never really caught on, because it was found to be easier to construct houses with higher eaves (see Fig. 9), and get almost the same advantage. Orientation east-west, on the other hand, is now universally accepted wherever it is possible and is considered essential for propagating houses. The cautionary words 'wherever possible' are put in because the commercial grower who has

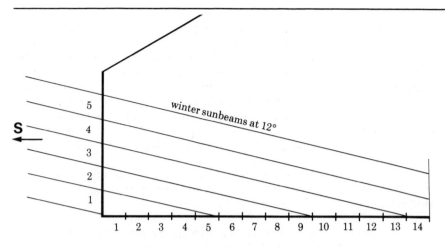

winter sunbeams at 12°

S ←

Fig. 8: winter light transmission through the south wall of an east-west oriented greenhouse. For every 4½ units of width the south wall should be one unit high in order to make best use of the winter sunshine.

several greenhouses faces a considerable problem. If he orientates his houses east–west the most southerly house will shade the one behind it and this in its turn, the next one, and so on. This dilemma can only be avoided by placing the houses sufficiently far apart to avoid mutual shading. This, unfortunately, is greedy of expensive land and increases heating costs, both installation and running costs. This kind of difficulty does not really concern the amateur who is rarely in a situation where he cannot orientate his greenhouse east–west.

If you wish to have two greenhouses and do not have sufficient room in the garden to site them so that no mutual shading occurs, then you are best advised to orientate them north–south as an adjacent pair.

Fig. 9: sunlight falling on a vinery-style greenhouse oriented east-west.

In winter the angle of incidence on the vertical south wall is 12°, at which light transmision is nearly 90%. But the angle of incidence on the 30° roof is 48°, at which light transmission is reduced to 85%.

In summer the angle of incidence is about 30° on both wall and roof, at which light transmission is nearly 90%.

Light transmission in winter can be improved by raising the height of the walls.

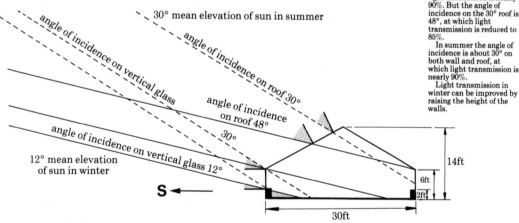

30° mean elevation of sun in summer

angle of incidence on vertical glass

angle of incidence on roof 30°

angle of incidence on roof 48°

30°

angle of incidence on vertical glass 12°

12° mean elevation of sun in winter

S ←

14ft

6ft

2ft

30ft

If the best possible greenhouse has been bought and orientated east–west with an unobstructed view of the southern sky, all the gains can be brought to nothing if the glass is allowed to become dirty. In urban areas, in spite of smoke abatement measures, glass will have become sufficiently dirty within about six weeks for 10 per cent of the available light to be lost, and in twice this length of time the loss could have reached 20 per cent.

It all starts with dust settling on the glass. This happens very quickly and after a few days it starts to bond together onto the glass to form a skin which requires the physical effort of wet brushing to remove it. In urban areas, effluent from chimney and car exhausts adds to the dust an oily

Dirty glass

ingredient (like traffic film) making the deposit even more difficult to shift. In the country the problem is by no means absent. The dust settles just the same and very soon forms a surface on which algae can take hold to form a green film, and where the glass abuts to the glazing bar and water lingers even moss will start to appear. This 'country dirt' is just as opaque as 'town dirt' and as difficult to shift. The only cure, albeit a temporary one, is to scrub the glass clean with a stiff brush or broom. (Detergent may be needed for town dirt.) Prevention is by far the best answer, and can be achieved by frequent hosing down of the glass before the dust has had time to stick firmly to it.

Keeping the inside of the greenhouse clean is less important for light transmission, but is a task that will be done regularly by the conscientious gardener.

Diffused and direct light

The 'doubting Thomases' may well say that their greenhouse is obstructed to the south and the glass is not all that clean, yet there is still plenty of light in it. This is perfectly true because they are talking about diffused or reflected light which comes in through the glass from all parts of the sky. It has never been possible to say precisely to what extent diffused light assists the plants to grow. It certainly does not give the leaves anything like the same amount of light energy as direct light, as can readily be demonstrated by bringing a plant from where it can receive direct unimpeded light into a well-lit room in a house, and watching its deterioration. All the evidence we have confirms beyond doubt that it is direct sunshine which is all-important in making plants grow, and the greenhouse gardener who grows plants under glass must make this the first article of his faith.

Chapter 3

Types of small greenhouse

Greenhouses were traditionally constructed from selected well-seasoned softwood. This was cheap, plentiful and readily machined to give lengths of timber with variable cross-sectional shapes (see Fig. 10). Two kinds of timber proved themselves superior for the purpose: the first, Baltic Redwood, is the wood of the Scots Pine (*Pinus sylvestris*), but comes from continental Europe; and the second, British Columbian pine (*Pseudotsuga taxifolia*), comes from Canada.

Timber

Baltic Redwood is of even grain, easily nailed without splitting and with good strength-to-weight ratio, enabling load-bearing members to have relatively small cross-sectional areas. British Columbian pine has the disadvantages that it splits easily when nailed, has a lifting grain when planed and does not readily absorb preservatives, but its great advantage is that it can be obtained in long straight-grained lengths. A common joinery timber that should be avoided because it has a very low durability is deal or whitewood, the timber of Norway Spruce (*Picea abies*).

Timber is now very expensive, but its main drawback is that being an organic material it will rot, or in modern jargon is biodegradable, unless carefully preserved and protected. Wood for greenhouses is usually protected by means of painting. The first coat, or primer, is of a paint made of linseed oil and white lead which is well worked into all surfaces and joints. It is the most important coat and provides a seal round the timber to protect it both from rot-causing fungi and from absorbing water. After the primer, an undercoat is applied to provide the correct colour base for the topcoat. In the case of greenhouses the topcoat will be white in order to give maximum reflection of light, but even so it is usual to tint the undercoat slightly so that any areas missed when applying the topcoat will readily show, and enable an even cover to be obtained. Many modern priming paints are not lead-based but they appear to be equally or even

Fig. 10 cross-sections of some common timber members of an English greenhouse.

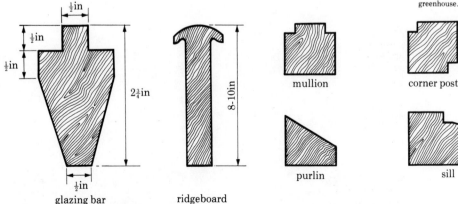

glazing bar

ridgeboard

mullion

corner post

purlin

sill

more satisfactory. Topcoats have a gloss finish which makes them water-repellent.

Paints are themselves biodegradable, and after three or four years they crack and flake and so need rubbing down and repainting to protect the priming underneath. Paint is only effective so long as it provides a seal and failure to maintain this quickly leads to deterioration of the wood.

To guard against the shortcomings of paint it is highly desirable that softwood is given preservative treatment before painting commences. The amateur is restricted to brushing or spraying wood with a copper-based preservative. This must be applied liberally, particularly to the ends of all pieces before they are erected. When the preservative is dry the painting can begin. However, it is possible to purchase worked timber impregnated with fungicidal and insecticidal preservatives. Such wood is described as having been 'pressure-treated'. It has a very long life particularly if subsequently painted. If pressure-treated timber is sawn the ends must be dipped in a copper preservative.

Western Red Cedar *(Thuja plicata),* although now expensive, is popular for small greenhouses. It is known as cedarwood, is of attractive appearance and does not need painting or preserving. It is a weak timber and consequently unsuitable for large houses. It splits easily and as it will remain unpainted only non-corrosive nails or screws should be used. The same applies to teak except that its cost is such that its use is virtually extinct.

Styles of greenhouse

There are two styles of modern greenhouse: the first is often described as an English greenhouse, and the second is known as a Dutch light house.

The English greenhouse usually stands on low brick walls, its woodwork is painted white and glazed with overlapping sheets of glass set in putty and secured with sprigs. Provided it has sheets of glass 600 × 600 mm (*2 ft × 2 ft*) it has much to commend it, except the disadvantage of having to paint it inside and out every third year.

Aluminium-alloy greenhouses are constructed in the style of the English greenhouse. Their advantage of high light transmission has already been stressed but the fact that they do not require any painting makes them highly attractive. The overlapping sheets of glass usually rest on plastic cushions and are secured by stainless-steel clips or metal clamping strips. They are mass-produced and are, therefore, highly competitive in price.

Two all-metal English-style greenhouses in an amateur's garden. These are full of plants, all arranged in a tidy fashion, and the whole is scrupulously clean in the interests of good hygiene.

The second style is the Dutch light house which is of less pleasing appearance. It is usually assembled from prefabricated frames of pressure-treated timber glazed with sheets of Dutch light glass and all supplied as a kit. Precast concrete slabs are usually included and form the base on which the house stands. The sheets of glass slide into the wooden frames and are secured by wooden cleats, nailed onto the frame with galvanised nails. Putty is not required. Dutch light houses are very serviceable. The pressure-treated timber never requires painting and has a known life of thirty years. Also it is a relatively simple matter to take the house to pieces and re-assemble it on another site if the need arises.

There are then three choices: English greenhouses, pleasing in appearance, but which must be painted both inside and out at regular and frequent intervals; Dutch light houses with the advantages of relative cheapness, low maintenance and excellent light transmission; aluminium alloy houses, easily cleaned with virtually no maintenance and good light transmission. The latter two have really superseded the first, but the choice between them to some extent depends upon the purpose to which the house is to be put; the Dutch light type is highly suitable for tomatoes, cucumbers and lettuce grown as unheated crops, and the aluminium-alloy house comes into its own if it is to be heated or if it is intended to provide it with staging for plants in containers.

Both Dutch light and metal houses can be obtained in the so-called 'Gazebo style' (Fig. 11) which is very useful for small gardens where space is at a premium. A domed house in the metal range is of geodetic design and is again especially useful for small areas.

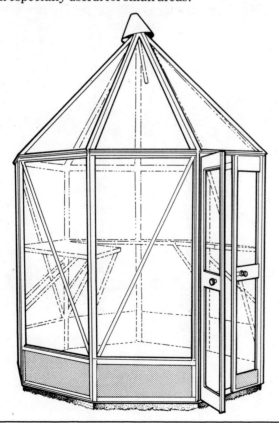

Fig. 11: gazebo-style greenhouse.

It is impossible to give prices for the different types of greenhouse because of the effects of inflation, quality differences between manufacturers and the increasing costs per unit area the smaller the house becomes. Some guidance may come from some rather generalised statistics which have averaged the list prices of small greenhouses and presented them on a percentage basis.

If the cost per square metre of a Dutch light house is taken as 100 per cent, then the comparisons are as follows:

Dutch light house	100%
Traditional English (softwood)	107%
Traditional English (Western Red Cedar)	112%
Aluminium alloy	93%

The round, tower or gazebo style of greenhouse which has excellent properties of light transmission and can be accommodated in a very small area.

These figures exclude delivery, site work, erection, painting and glazing. When these are taken into account the disparity between the traditional English types and the others is increased.

Chapter 4

Plastic structures

Plastic film is often described as a glass-substitute and to some extent this is true, although enthusiasts prefer to think of it as a substance in its own right commanding its own disciplines within horticulture.

The best known, cheapest and most widely used of all is, of course, polyethylene chloride, better known as 'polythene'. The low-density form of the material which is used in horticulture is naturally flexible, and although not biodegradable it rapidly deteriorates under the influence of ultra-violet light to become brittle and readily torn, particularly so at warmer temperatures. To delay deterioration horticultural polythene has ultra-violet-light absorbers added to it during manufacture. The fact that it then no longer allows ultra-violet light to be transmitted through it is of no consequence as in this respect it is comparable with glass. Another of its advantages is that it remains flexible over the range of temperatures which occur in temperate countries (middle latitude climate).

It transmits about 86 per cent of the visible light and so compares well with glass which transmits about 90 per cent, and also allows nearly 80 per cent of the radiant heat from the sun to pass through it. Unlike glass it allows the long-wave radiation from the earth to pass through it readily, so that on clear nights the temperatures in polythene houses drop rapidly and on occasions a lower temperature has been recorded inside the house than the air temperature outside. This fact, while it is a considerable disadvantage when it comes to frost protection, also means that the greenhouse effect is reduced so that 'poly-houses' do not get as hot as glasshouses in bright sunshine and thus can manage with less ventilation.

Finally polythene has the special properties of being permeable to oxygen and carbon dioxide and almost impermeable to water. It is these qualities which make it such a useful material for covering seed trays, sealing grafts, air layers and beds or boxes of cuttings.

Polyvinyl chloride (PVC) is also a well-known material. It is a rigid

The interior of a walk-in polythene tunnel, which in this case is being used for growing-on nursery stock but could equally well be used for the production of lettuces, tomatoes, or other food crops. The circular hole in the polythene is for ventilation.

material but can be plasticised to produce a flexible film. Like polythene it deteriorates under the influence of ultra-violet light and if used as a cladding material for plant houses has to have ultra-violet absorbers added during manufacture. It has a longer life than polythene, some claiming it to be twice as long. It transmits light marginally better but transmits radiant heat to a much lesser extent. Because of this the long-wave heat radiation from the soil it covers is largely held back thus giving much warmer conditions at night, particularly on clear nights. It is only slightly permeable to oxygen and carbon dioxide and is, therefore, of much less use to the propagator. PVC is more expensive than polythene and has not seriously rivalled it.

There are a number of other clear plastic films with interesting properties but it is beyond the scope of this book to describe them as they are still subject to trial and experiment. At the moment it seems unlikely that polythene will be superseded.

When polythene was first used as a glass substitute it was on structures of more or less orthodox greenhouse design where it performed well enough except that it was very prone to deterioration where it passed over wooden supports and could become very warm in sunshine. As time went by the small plastic cloche, or tunnel, which had achieved considerable success, was enlarged into the 'walk-in' tunnel. This was originally a semi-circle 4.3 m (*14 ft*) wide and half as high, but is now available in a variety of widths up to 9 m (*30 ft*). Such tunnels are covered with 500 or 600 gauge polythene and are available from many manufacturers.

Walk-in tunnels are used in commerce for the production of lettuces

Fig. 12: walk-in plastic tunnel.

(sometimes throughout the whole year), tomatoes, peppers and other crops, and by nurserymen both for propagation from cuttings and for raising young plants in containers. For the amateur gardener a walk-in tunnel is not without its attractions for use as an unheated structure for growing tomatoes or any plant that might otherwise be grown in a cold greenhouse. There is the attraction of the low capital cost compared with glass and the ease with which it can be erected on a fresh site in order to avoid soil problems. The possibility of heating is not ruled out but, on the other hand, it runs somewhat counter to the low-cost production concept by which tunnels are characterised. The modern tunnels can be fitted with ventilation provision, proper doors and so on. The life of the cladding does not normally exceed 18 months, and its replacement should really be regarded as an annual maintenance routine.

One interesting idea for plastic houses was the 'bubble' house, consisting of a single large sheet inflated with air by means of a pump. Several were constructed for trial purposes but proved to have shortcomings which eventually led to their abandonment. Other sophistications are double-skinned houses where a layer of air between the two skins acts as an insulator and reduces considerably the radiation and conduction losses. In some versions the two skins are kept apart by tension of the film over separators, and in some sophisticated designs by pressurised air from a pump.

The plastic house or structure is still in the developmental stage, and it is possible that further advances will be made. It is difficult, however, to see how the curvilinear tunnel with its excellent light-transmitting properties could be improved upon.

Trials are now in progress to evaluate the use of rigid plastic sheets as an alternative to glass on greenhouses of permanent and conventional construction. The cladding is fabricated in the form of panels consisting of two or three sheets of rigid plastic (polycarbonate) sealed all round their edges to provide condensation-proof and dust-proof double or triple glazing. Greenhouses so cladded have extremely good properties of heat retention when compared with those using glass, which compensates for their higher costs of construction: so their ultimate success will depend upon the lasting qualities of the plastic in respect of light and temperature.

Polythene film is available as follows:

1. 600 gauge ($150 \mu m$) containing an ultra-violet-light inhibitor and used for tunnel houses. Sizes of sheet normally quoted are:

6.5 × 50 m	21.3 × 164 ft
7.5 × 50 m	24.6 × 164 ft
9.25 × 40 m	30.3 × 131.2 ft
11.25 × 40 m	36.9 × 131.2 ft

2. 500 gauge ($125 \mu m$) containing an ultra-violet-light inhibitor and used for the same purposes as 600 gauge, which has now largely superseded it because of its greater strength and longer life (two years).

3. 150 gauge ($38 \mu m$) used for a variety of purposes, e.g. covering seed containers and cuttings. It is available as clear, opaque, green and black film; one type used for greenhouse lining is treated to reduce condensation.

4. 200 gauge ($50 \mu m$), dense black, used for blacking-out plants for day-length control.

5. Bubble polythene, a film containing air bubbles and used for lining greenhouses for fuel saving in winter.

Chapter 5

Heating and ventilation

Heating greenhouses makes it possible to extend the range of plants grown as well as making their yields earlier and greater. The advantage, however, is one for which a fairly high price has to be paid. Tables in Appendix I show comparisons of estimated heating costs using different heat sources. In the United Kingdom gas is the cheapest, oil and solid fuel are more expensive and electricity has become too expensive to be considered. Oil and gas systems have advantages over solid fuel: they are more convenient to manage, and have a very rapid response to automatic controls. It is, of course, possible to heat greenhouses from an extension of a domestic central-heating system, a method which avoids the cost of a separate boiler and boiler house.

Heat can be supplied to the greenhouse in various ways. When using fossil fuels (coal, oil, gas) it is usual to burn the fuel outside the greenhouse in a furnace, known as the boiler, and to convey the heat produced, or as much of it as possible, into the house by means of hot water or steam. The heat then passes into the atmosphere of the greenhouse through the walls of the pipes which carry the water or steam. The steam will condense back into water and will be returned to the boiler, or the water will return to be re-heated.

Fig. 13: diagrammatic representation of a hot-water heating system. The height of the header tank above the boiler determines the water-pressure in the system.

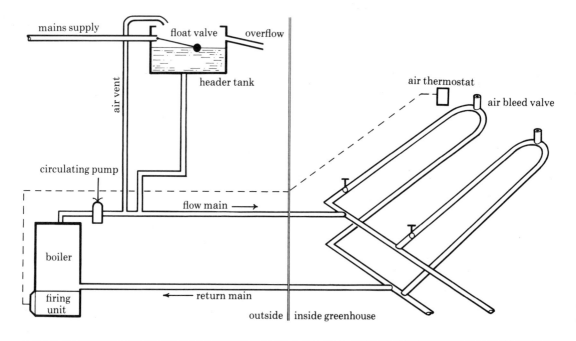

mains supply

float valve overflow

air vent

header tank

air thermostat

air bleed valve

circulating pump

flow main →

boiler

firing unit

← return main

outside ‖ inside greenhouse

The size of the pipes through which hot water circulates has a profound effect on the properties of the heating system. The 100 mm (*4 in*) diameter cast-iron pipes which were used almost universally until the 1950s give a system with what is called 'high thermal inertia'. This means that the system contains a large amount of water which takes a long time to heat and an equally long time to cool down, and is thus slow to respond to automatic control. Modern systems use small-bore pipes made of mild steel with diameters of 38 mm (*1½ in*) or less. Such systems hold a small amount of water and heat and cool rapidly, that is to say they have a low thermal inertia and are thus highly responsive to automatic control. Because of the greater viscous resistance that small pipes offer to the flow of water, an electric pump is essential to bring about the rapid circulation of the water required. Small-bore systems are usually described as high-speed hot water systems and are very similar to modern central-heating systems.

Another method is to circulate the air in the glasshouse through a heater by means of a fan. In large commercial glasshouses the air is sometimes circulated through ducts made with plastic film from which it escapes at intervals through holes along their lengths. Air heating systems, using fan electrical heaters, have been used in garden greenhouses but because of the higher cost of electricity their popularity is in decline.

An attractive alternative to heating systems which require the installation of heating pipes is that of natural-gas heaters. These stand in the centre of the greenhouse, and are chimneyless. They require no connections other than to a gas main. Pilot flames ignite the gas when the thermostat indicates that heat is required. The gas burns completely, producing carbon dioxide and water as the combustion products. The former assists the plants in efficient photosynthesis, and the water vapour increases the relative humidity. Condensation may be an inconvenient consequence when the temperature falls. There is negligible danger from phytotoxic waste products of combustion such as carbon monoxide or sulphur dioxide. Householders with gas central-heating systems who benefit from special tariff arrangements will find natural gas an attractive proposition. Before committing yourself to a direct gas-fired heater, however, you would be well advised to check that the cost of the heater is less than the cost of extending your domestic heating system into the greenhouse.

Bear in mind also that some efficiency is lost at the lower end of the greenhouse temperature range—below 10°C (*50°F*)—because of the pilot-jet gas consumption.

Various units are available with different ratings. The 3 kW (*10,000 Btu*) is the most widely supplied.

Propane heaters are worth considering in areas where natural gas is not available. The gas cylinders require to be fitted with a pressure-regulating valve. 'Bottled' gas is much more expensive than natural gas, but competitive in price compared with electricity.

Great caution must be exercised in the use of any chimneyless paraffin heater which burns inside the greenhouse, because unless the burner mechanism is such that total combustion of the fuel takes place the plants will be killed by carbon monoxide poisoning. Only the highest grade of paraffin can be used, in which the sulphur content is low enough to prevent the formation of levels of sulphur dioxide sufficient to be phytotoxic (poisonous to plants).

A direct gas-fired greenhouse heater. In such heaters combustion is complete, there are no toxic waste products, and, because the heater is inside the greenhouse and does not have a flue, the efficiency is extremely high.

Heat loss The heat that is released into the greenhouse by the heating system is lost to the outside atmosphere by convection of the warm air through the overlaps in the glass. This loss is greatest when it is dry and windy and least when it is wet and still because then water tends to seal the gap where the sheets of glass overlap. Losses also take place by conduction of the heat through the shell of the house, a loss that is roughly proportional to the difference between the inside and outside temperatures. Finally heat is lost by radiation, which is greatest during clear nights and least during cloudy ones.

The total heat loss from the house per hour represents the amount of heat which must be put into it in order to maintain a steady temperature. There are simple methods for calculating heat requirements and these are explained in Appendix I.

During the daytime when the house needs to have as much light entering it as possible nothing very much can be done to reduce heat losses, other than the creation of some kind of shelter to reduce windspeed. Cold winds greatly increase heat loss, and shelter belts of trees and hedges acting as a windbreak have a considerable effect in reducing heat loss. They must not, however, intercept the light from the sun or any gain provided in fuel saving is lost by the shade they cast. At night the erection of a screen a few inches away from the glass brings about a very substantial reduction in heat loss. Much effort is being expended by engineers to devise effective means of installing thermal screens, as they are called, which can be put automatically into position at dusk and similarly removed at dawn. Polythene and other plastic film, and special fabricated plastic cloths, are all effective but plastic film is the cheapest. It is not too difficult for the amateur to install a thermal screen of plastic film suspended over his crop during the hours of darkness, at times of the year when heat losses are high.

Thermostats It is very necessary these days because of the high cost of all fuels to have a heating system that is controlled automatically so that as soon as the desired temperature is reached the burner is shut off until heat is required again. Therefore it is necessary to install a thermostat to control the boiler. This is simple enough if oil or gas boilers are being used but is rather more difficult when solid fuel is used, for the simple reason that a coal fire cannot be switched off and on like gas or oil burners. It must be allowed to die down but given enough fuel and air to keep it alight and hot enough to prevent corrosion of the boiler.

Thermostats must be positioned carefully so that they control the temperature of the greenhouse where the plants are actually growing, but more important is the necessity of protecting them from radiation effects. During the daytime an unprotected thermostat is receiving radiation from the sun which may cause it to become warmer than the surrounding air by as much as $6\,C°$ ($10\,F°$), thus shutting off the heat supply before it should; but, much more seriously, at night-time it is radiating heat itself and so may become much colder than the surrounding air, thus bringing on the heating system before it is necessary. Not only does this prove expensive, but it results in incorrect temperatures in the greenhouse.

This difficulty is avoided by housing thermostats and thermometers in what are called aspirated screens (Fig. 14). An aspirated screen is an insulated box, covered with metal or foil to reflect radiation. A small electric fan sucks air out of the box, which enters it through a louvre at its

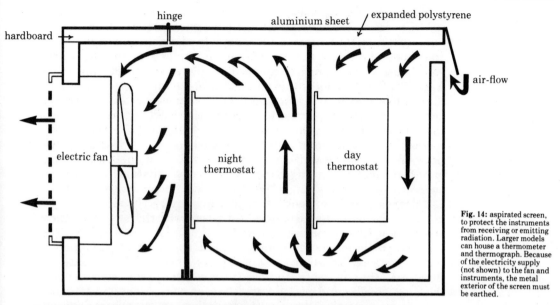

hardboard

hinge

aluminium sheet

expanded polystyrene

air-flow

electric fan

night
thermostat

day
thermostat

Fig. 14: aspirated screen,
to protect the instruments
from receiving or emitting
radiation. Larger models
can house a thermometer
and thermograph. Because
of the electricity supply
(not shown) to the fan and
instruments, the metal
exterior of the screen must
be earthed.

other end so that a sample of the greenhouse air is flowing over the
instruments. These are then able accurately to measure ambient
temperatures. Aspirated screens suitable for amateurs are available.

Ventilation

Much mystery used to surround the subject of ventilation of greenhouses,
but the facts are quite simple. Ventilators exist for the sole purpose of
providing openings through which excess heat in the house can be
dissipated. The other advantages which follow are purely incidental but
nonetheless useful.

When a ventilator on the ridge of a house is opened the more buoyant
warm air floats up through it and its place is taken by colder air from
outside. This air has to come in through the overlaps in the glass and round
the edges of doors, or sinks in through the ventilator opening past the
warm air which is going out.

If as well as having ventilators at the ridge of the house there are also
ventilators in the walls as low as possible; then the warm air escapes
through the ridge vents and the cool air comes in through the side ones,
creating what is called the 'chimney effect' and making the whole
ventilation process much quicker and more effective.

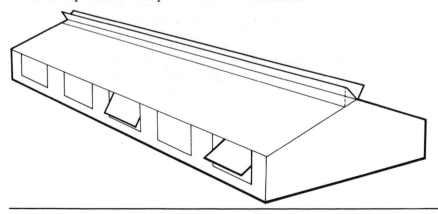

Fig. 15: modern
greenhouses have
continuous ventilators
which open through 60°
and which give a larger
total aperture than single
vents.

In designing a greenhouse the provision made for ventilation needs to be sufficient to cool the house to within a few degrees of the outside temperature on the hottest summer days. In a large commercial greenhouse this means enough ventilator openings to permit the entire greenhouse atmosphere to be changed completely once every minute (see Appendix IV). To achieve the same degree of cooling in a very small house the rate has to go up to as much as once every three-quarters of a minute because the smaller the house the more ventilation it requires to achieve the same result. Ideally the greenhouse should be built with ventilators each side of the ridge running the entire length of the roof with a number of side vents in both side walls. As few houses are built with such generous provision, amateurs are urged to provide extra ventilation by securing the doors in an open position in hot weather. Sliding doors are particularly useful for this purpose. Ventilation, in many ways, is the opposite of heating: ventilation has to be designed to cope with the hottest weather and heating with the coldest.

As most of the excess heat which ventilation is designed to dissipate comes from solar radiation, i.e. sunshine, and this tends to fluctuate throughout the day, ventilators need to be constantly adjusted. In practice this is not possible and has led commercial growers to invest in automatic ventilation equipment. Automatic ventilation controls are available for small greenhouses and are well worth considering.

Before the need for adequate ventilation became properly understood in the early 1950s, greenhouses were built with totally inadequate ventilation and to prevent over-heating in sunny weather shading the houses with whitening was the rule. This was unsatisfactory because the shading excluded the light essential for proper development of the crop. Shading is nowadays regarded by the professional gardener as something required only by plants which naturally grow in shade or by cuttings in the process of rooting.

The incidental advantages of ventilation must be understood. The first of these is that the air contains a small amount of carbon dioxide (0.03 per cent or 300 parts per million) which is essential for plants if they are to photosynthesise at the maximum rate possible in the prevailing light intensity and temperature level. When the air is still the carbon dioxide in the atmosphere surrounding the leaf becomes depleted and photosynthesis slows down. The movement of air through the foliage caused by ventilation maintains the concentration at the normal level. Commercial growers even go to the extent of enriching the atmosphere of their houses with carbon dioxide from artificial sources.

Ventilation also has the effect of reducing relative humidity in the greenhouse to a level close to that of the external atmosphere (but only when the latter is lower than that of the house). This lowering of relative humidity is desirable because it can prevent the condensation of water on the internal surfaces of the house should the temperature suddenly drop. The existence of still moist air around the plants is ideal for the germination of fungus spores, but this will not occur when ventilation is taking place.

Ventilation is quite a problem for the amateur gardener and tedious to monitor, but the golden rule is to err on the side of generosity throughout the summer.

Chapter 6

The greenhouse soil

If a greenhouse is built on an area of soil not previously used for such a purpose it is invariably found that no matter what is grown in it the first year's crop is magnificent but subsequent ones deteriorate until they become totally unacceptable. This decline in soil fertility is called 'soil sickness' or (by tomato growers, who were the first to experience it) 'tomato sickness'.

For many years the cause of this problem was a mystery and ingenious theories were advanced to account for it. The mystery is now fairly well solved; the trouble does not have a simple cause; it is a combination of a number of factors of which some or all may apply.

The soil is a medium that teems with life, both animal and plant, most of it microscopic; a population so varied and so well balanced that it is difficult to imagine. This population of soil micro-organisms performs a number of functions, most significant among which is the total destruction of all dead organic matter. This matter is finally resolved into simple gases and soil minerals, in the course of which process all the plant nutrients such as nitrogen, phosphorus and potassium are re-cycled for use by subsequent generations of plants.

Among this vast multifarious soil population it is not surprising to find a few out-and-out rogues and some others normally law-abiding but in circumstances of great temptation liable to undesirable conduct. The former are called plant parasites and the latter facultative parasites. While the term 'parasite' is familiar enough, that of 'facultative parasite' needs explaining. They are organisms which normally live on dead organic matter but possess the ability in certain circumstances to attack living plants.

In normal circumstances all the species of soil micro-organisms are in such a state of competition for available resources that their numbers remain in a state of reasonable balance. As soon as a glasshouse is placed over the soil, conditions cease to be normal. To begin with, the temperature becomes higher; a crop such as tomatoes will be planted to the exclusion of all else giving a high density of a single kind of root; the addition of optimum quantities of fertilisers and manure and regular watering will all provide conditions which encourage a high rate of activity on the part of the soil micro-organisms. The high density of tomato roots encourages any parasites of their roots to multiply and the increased rate of activity may encourage the facultative parasites to turn from their normal harmless state to being harmful. We are mainly talking about root-attacking fungi, although the same applies to various animal foes such as certain eelworms, insects and slugs. The second year in which the same crop is grown the process is repeated, and the effect is cumulative, so after a few years the plant's roots are destroyed faster than they can be produced and it has difficulty in surviving. Although the problem was first

Soil sickness

A symphilid (magnification ×100) — a soil pest of heated greenhouses, which is controlled by soil sterilisation. Symphilids may be present in compost made from unsterilised loam.

These almost microscopic pests are known as springtails or *Collembola*. They can be present in vast numbers and cause serious damage to plants growing in the soil or in soil-based compost. They are readily destroyed by soil-sterilising procedures, but when these are not available chemical methods may be used.

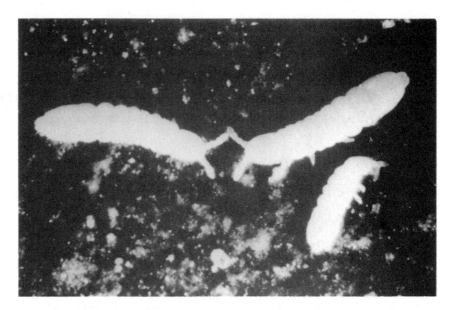

encountered with tomatoes it applies to any plant repeatedly grown as a crop on the same site; the technical term is 'monocropping'.

The tomato grower originally overcame the problem by removing all the soil in the greenhouse to a depth of a foot and replacing it with fresh. This tedious and expensive expedient was ultimately replaced by a process known as partial steam sterilisation. To accomplish this, steam is injected into the soil so that the top 380 mm (*15 in*) is heated to a temperature of 100°C (*212°F*), then allowed to cool down. This drastic treatment has a remarkable effect on soil fertility which leaps back to a level even higher than it was originally. The effect of heat is to kill the entire population of soil animals, most of the soil fungi and bacteria and all weed seeds. Certain soil bacteria do survive, and prominent among these are the ammonifying bacteria which play a vital role in the nitrogen cycle because they are the agents responsible for converting the nitrogen in organic matter into inorganic ammonia. Unfortunately, after steaming re-infection causes soil sickness to return quite rapidly, necessitating annual repetition of the treatment if high yields are to be maintained. As the cost of fuel and labour rose the tomato grower became desperate to devise techniques whereby he could abandon the soil totally as a medium in which to grow his plants, as the cucumber grower had done from the very beginning, although for different reasons. The answer eventually came with the peat bag on the one hand, and with sophisticated hydroponic techniques, such as 'nutrient film technique' and 'rockwool beds', on the other. On the way to reaching this recent answer chemical sterilisation was often used as an alternative to steaming, but always had the disadvantage that it took a greenhouse out of commission for longer than the commercial grower liked. Methyl bromide clears rapidly from the soil but it is so dangerous that it can be used only by qualified contractors.

Where in all this does the amateur gardener stand? He wants to use his greenhouse for growing tomatoes and lettuces, or anything else normally grown in the soil as distinct from a container. There is little doubt that he can start off in the soil, but after a couple of years, if he does not want to change the soil or move the greenhouse to a fresh site, the peat bag is his answer and at the present time it is difficult to see how a better or more convenient method could arise. Chemical treatment is one answer he might wish to keep in mind; the only substance which he can use being one called 'dazomet' which is sold under a number of proprietary names. Household disinfectant has many adherents among an older generation of gardeners but has a very limited range of troubles against which it is effective.

Soil sickness, though mainly a response to monocropping, can be compounded by two other problems which though distinct are related. The first is soil moisture content. The driest parts of the British Isles enjoy an annual rainfall of about 560 mm of rain per year (*22 in*) of which about half percolates down through the soil to drainage. In most of the rest of the UK the quantity is greater. This percolating water not only charges the soil with water to a considerable depth but also removes soluble materials from its surface levels to lower ones and perhaps out of it altogether into the drainage system. In the greenhouse rainfall does not occur, so in order to recharge the soil with water to the depth which roots will inhabit, it is necessary to apply substantial amounts of water when preparing it for planting, to ensure that this occurs. For rough and ready reckoning it can be assumed that 25 mm of water (*1 in*) is sufficient to wet the soil to a depth of 255 mm (*10 in*) and that five times this amount should be applied, which is about 125 litres per square metre (*24 gall per sq yd*); a surprisingly large amount when it comes to applying it. It is, of course, most easily done by means of an irrigation system or at least a hosepipe with a sprinkler. The flow rate of the hosepipe should be checked first by noting the time taken for the sprinkler to fill a bucket and then calculating the time it will take to deliver the required amount of water. Use the formula:

Moisture content

$$\frac{\text{Time taken to fill bucket (in minutes)} \times \text{amount of water required}}{\text{capacity of bucket}}$$

which will give the answer in minutes.

The second and related problem is that of the concentration of soluble salts in the soil moisture. Although its significance was not realised until the early 1950s it had undoubtedly been responsible for many previously unexplained crop failures. It simply means that the quantity of nitrates which has accumulated in the top spit of the soil is such that the plants' uptake of water and nutrients other than nitrogen is impeded and certain unmistakable symptoms of ill health become apparent. The concentration of salts was first measured on a scale known as the pC scale ('p' indicates that it is logarithmic and 'C' stands for conductivity) and later by one known as the CF scale ('C' = conductivity and 'F' = factor) and ever since greenhouse growers have referred to the pC problem or the CF problem.

Soluble salts

Amateurs are just as likely to encounter the problem as professionals but they can avoid it completely if they practise flooding, as described above, before planting a crop, and do not apply fertilisers at a rate greater than that recommended. Incidentally, lettuces, tomatoes and cucumbers are very sensitive to high soluble-salt concentrations (see Appendix V).

Chapter 7

Seed and potting composts

Gardeners have been growing plants in pots and boxes for a long time and they soon learned that garden soil was not satisfactory for the purpose unless it was considerably modified. To begin with, ordinary garden soil is not sufficiently open to allow water to percolate through it at the required rate. This meant that some gritty material like sand had to be added. Next, when wetted its water-holding capacity (container capacity) is insufficient and this has to be increased by adding some spongy material of an organic nature, like leafmould, decomposed manure or peat. Even with these additions the mixture, or compost as gardeners call it, is not satisfactory unless the soil selected has certain characteristics: it has to be one in which none of its mineral component parts, i.e. sand, silt and clay, are present in such quantities that one or the other stamps its presence too strongly; soils of this equable type are described as loams and so the soil component of a compost is always referred to as loam. When loam, sand and peat are mixed together the compost is still unlikely to have a sufficient reserve of plant nutrients and these must finally be added. If the compost, now complete, is put in a container and watered it will produce a crop of weeds which will compete and interfere with the germinating seeds or whatever has been planted so carefully, while at the same time soil-borne pests and diseases will be attacking everything that grows. This state of affairs can only be avoided by sterilising the loam in which these troubles are located.

This was the case in the 1930s when little or no scientific work had been undertaken to establish the optimum quantities of compost ingredients and the most suitable forms of each of the disinfecting procedures that should be undertaken. The task was tackled for the first time by Messrs Lawrence and Newall at the John Innes Horticultural Institution which was situated in Merton, England. After some years of painstaking work they were able to make recommendations for the preparation of standardised composts, which still hold good forty years later. Although details of these composts are readily available no apology is given for repeating them here. There are two composts, one for small and medium seeds, and one for large seeds and plants.

Seed Compost
Sterilised loam 2 parts by volume
Horticultural peat 1 part by volume
Sand (Sharp 3 mm grist) 1 part by volume
To each 100 litres (*bushel*) is added 117 g (*1½ oz*) of superphosphate and 58 g (*¾ oz*) of ground limestone.

NB: These metric and imperial quantities are not equivalent.

Potting Compost

Sterilised loam 7 parts by volume
Horticultural peat 3 parts by volume
Sand (Sharp 3 mm grist) 2 parts by volume

To each 100 litres (*bushel*) of the potting compost is added 310 g (*4 oz*) of John Innes base and 58 g ($\frac{3}{4}$ *oz*) of ground limestone to make what is called JIP 1.

If the quantities of base and chalk are doubled the compost is called JIP 2 and if trebled JIP 3.

The point of having three strengths, so to speak, is to allow for varying types of plant and seasons, e.g. JIP 1 is for slow growing plants at any time of the year and for other plants in the winter, JIP 2 is for spring and summer use for more vigorous plants, and JIP 3 for vigorous plants in the summer.

When amateurs read that the loam has to be sterilised they may feel that making 'John Innes' lies beyond their ability. This is not the case, however, because it is a relatively simple matter to make a steriliser that will sterilise small quantities of loam quickly and effectively (see Fig. 16). The greatest difficulty is likely to be that of obtaining suitable loam and, in many parts of the country, coarse sand, free from lime. Fine sand beloved of old time gardeners is not suitable for John Innes. John Innes base is a mixture which consists of:

Hoof and horn meal (14% N) 3 mm grist	2 parts by weight
Superphosphate (18% soluble phosphoric acid)	2 parts by weight
Potassium sulphate (48% K_2O)	1 part by weight

It is widely available as a ready-mixed commodity.

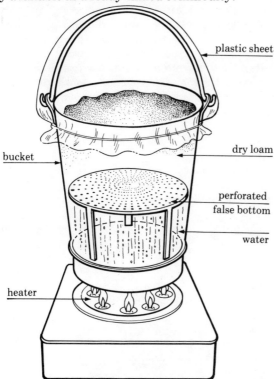

plastic sheet

dry loam

bucket

perforated
false bottom

water

heater

Fig. 16: a simple soil steriliser can be made by placing a perforated false bottom about one-third up inside the bucket. Sufficient water is added — one litre per nine litres of dry loam — and the bucket is placed over a gas ring or similar heater. A plastic sheet is tied over the top, and when this balloons out with steam the soil is sterilised.

If the soil in your garden is neither sandy nor contains too much clay, it will probably make a reasonable compost. If this is not the case the amateur must fall back on loamless composts. The traditional test for gauging the suitability of loam for compost purposes is to squeeze a quantity of it in the hand when it is moist, but not wet. When the pressure of the hand is released it should hold together but shatter if dropped. When in a lump it should, if stroked with a wet thumb, show a 'greased' track, but not a 'polished' one. These rough and ready tests help to assess the clay content to establish that it is neither excessive nor deficient. Gardeners of an earlier generation would cut and stack for at least six months turf from old pastures, such soil usually having excellent 'crumb structure'. The period of six months provided an opportunity for all the roots and herbage to decompose. Apart from the physical properties of a loam sample, it must not have too high a lime content or this may cause complications later with certain plants. A slightly acid loam is to be preferred.

Although for most purposes loam-based John Innes composts cannot be beaten, especially for amateur gardeners, a vast number of plants are now grown in loamless composts. These were developed in the USA and have been widely adopted in Britain by growers who had difficulty in obtaining suitable loam for John Innes and who wanted to avoid the chore of steam sterilising. In Britain loamless composts usually consist of peat or mixtures of peat and fine sand to which have been added a range of fertilisers. In the United States and Australia composts made of shredded bark or sawdust are in common use and give excellent results, but where good peat is easily obtained they have not made much impact.

Peat composts are now marketed by many firms under their own brand names and their compositions are not known precisely, because the manufacturers do not divulge them. Suffice it to say that they are usually peat or peat/sand mixes to which the appropriate range of fertilisers has been added. For those who want to do it themselves the Glasshouse Crop Research Institute has investigated the composition of peat-based composts and has stated that a well-designed one will produce plants as good as in John Innes, but that the management of plants in them is more exacting. The mixtures they recommend, which are known as GCRI composts, are as follows:

Seed Compost
Granular horticultural peat 1 part by volume
Lime-free fine sand (0.05–0.5 mm particles) 1 part by volume
To each 100 litres (*bushel*) is added: 40 g ($\frac{1}{2}$ *oz*) ammonium sulphate
80 g (*1 oz*) 18% superphosphate
40 g ($\frac{1}{2}$ *oz*) potassium sulphate
310 g (*4 oz*) ground limestone
(calcium carbonate)

Potting Compost
Granular horticultural peat 3 parts by volume
Lime-free fine sand (0.05–0.5 mm particles) 1 part by volume
To each 100 litres (*bushel*) is added: 155 g (*2 oz*) 18% superphosphate
235 g (*3 oz*) ground limestone
235 g (*3 oz*) dolomitic limestone (calcium magnesium carbonate)
40 g ($\frac{1}{2}$ *oz*) Frit No. 253A

If the compost is to be used immediately, or within a short time, the following must be added:

20 g ($\frac{1}{4}$ oz) ammonium nitrate
40 g ($\frac{1}{2}$ oz) urea-formaldehyde
80 g (1 oz) potassium sulphate

If, on the other hand, it cannot be used fairly quickly then instead the following are added:

40 g ($\frac{1}{2}$ oz) ammonium nitrate
80 g (1 oz) potassium nitrate

The list of additives looks frightening but, in fact, they are all common fertiliser materials easily purchased either as individual materials or proprietory mixtures. The Frit No 253A is absolutely vital as it contains all the trace elements (boron, zinc, manganese, iron, copper and molybdenum) which are needed in minute quantities and are difficult and dangerous to supply in any other way.

When plants are grown in containers they soon exhaust the nutrient reserves of the compost, a fact demonstrated by the slowing down of growth, a hardening of their tissues and a paling of their foliage. Before these symptoms of starvation are observed steps should have been taken to avoid it, either by liquid feeding or by moving the plant into a larger pot or planting it out. Liquid feeding is generally the most convenient method and will be discussed later when dealing with the various crops.

All 'growing media' as composts are frequently called must provide the correct physical conditions for root growth. If these are not correct no amount of fertiliser treatment can compensate. Experiments have shown that in a compost with a sub-standard physical condition, the difference in plant growth between a low standard of nutrition and a high one is no more than 12 per cent whereas with a compost of good physical condition, the difference rises to 91 per cent.

Good physical condition mainly refers to what is termed the air-filled porosity of a compost. This is the amount of air it contains after it has been saturated and drained back to 'container capacity', which is holding all the water it can against the pull of gravity, all drainage having ceased.

If the air-filled porosity drops below 10–15 per cent growth is affected and root-death occurs at the lower levels of the container. Above 15 per cent, roots can grow and function properly. Composts made from coarse sphagnum peat alone have an air-filled porosity of 30–40 per cent and made from the finer grades an air-filled porosity of 12–15 per cent.

Air-filled porosity is a function of the larger pore spaces within the compost, i.e. those greater than 60 microns (1 micron = 0.001 mm).

It has already been stressed that with loam compost coarse sand of 3 mm grist is used to increase air-filled porosity and sand of this size can be relied upon always to do this, whereas finer sands reduce it. In the case of the GCRI loamless composts the grade of sand recommended is much finer. Although its function is to make the compost heavier in weight (which it does by about 400 per cent) it will inevitably reduce the air-filled porosity of the peat, though not below the critical level if the correct grade of granular peat has been selected.

Whenever there is doubt about air-filled porosity of a compost a simple test can be conducted as follows:

1 Weigh a container and fill with compost consolidated as though it contained a plant.

2 Place the container in water (weighed down if necessary) until the compost is saturated.
3 Remove the container rapidly from the water and place in an empty bucket of known weight and weigh.
4 Immediately stand the container on a sand-base and allow to stand for twelve hours, then weigh again.
5 Mark the position inside the container reached by the compost, empty the container and line it with a thin polythene bag.
6 Fill the lined container with water to the level formerly reached by the compost and weigh.
7 Subtract the weight of the container from all three measurements.
8 Calculate the percentage of air-filled porosity using the formula:

$$\frac{(\text{weight of saturated compost} - \text{weight of drained compost}) \times 100}{\text{weight of water equal to the volume of the compost}}$$

If the calculation gives a value lower than 15 per cent suspicion must fall on the coarseness of the sand.

Specifications for compost ingredients always state that sands should be non-calcareous (lime-free). This is to prevent the use of materials which would cause the pH of the compost to rise. The pH scale describes the acidity or alkalinity of solutions. The letter 'p' indicates that the scale is logarithmic, meaning that each point on the scale represents an increase or decrease by a factor of 10. Loam composts are designed to have a pH of about 6.5, and as little as 0.5 per cent of calcium carbonate (lime) in a sand used for the GCRI composts can raise the alkalinity of the compost by pH 0.7, i.e. five times. This is quite critical because the neutral point of the pH scale is pH 7 and an increase of 0.7 takes the original pH of the compost from 6.5 to 7.2 which is well within the danger zone for many plants.

Chapter 8

Plants in containers

It is not so many years ago that to say 'plants in pots or boxes' would have sufficed. Today the range of 'things' in which plants are grown is so varied that the more general term 'container' now has to be used to cover all possibilities.

The traditional flower pot, made of baked unglazed clay, has virtually disappeared, having been superseded by the plastic pot. Plastic pots are usually rigid and made of polypropylene; they are not long lived because after a while they become hard and brittle, but being light, cheap and easily transported they have displaced the heavy and now very expensive clay pot.

The clay pot, being porous, has water evaporating from all of its surface which causes the compost in it to be slightly cooler than in a plastic pot of equivalent size; differences of $1.1C°$ ($2F°$) at night and $3.3C°$ ($6F°$) in the daytime having been recorded. Thus with higher temperatures and a slower moisture loss an overall gain in growth in plastic pots can occur.

Traditional practice was to 'crock' clay pots, i.e. broken pieces of pot were placed in the bottom over the drainage hole (see Fig 17). It was always difficult to find out from gardeners why this was done but one was usually told that it aided drainage, aided aeration and prevented earthworms getting into the compost. All these reasons have been shown to be fallacious and the practice has now died out almost totally.

A range of plant containers, both durable and biodegradable. On the right of the front row is a rockwool block for hydroponic growing methods.

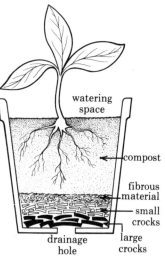

watering
space

compost

fibrous
material

small
crocks

large
crocks

drainage
hole

Fig. 17: this traditional method of crocking a flower-pot is now known to impede drainage rather than to assist it, and is thus no longer used by modern gardeners.

The Jiffy pot, made from peat enclosed within a mesh. It is bought in the dehydrated form, the disc on the left; after immersion in water it swells to form the container depicted in the middle of the photograph; and on the right a young begonia is seen well established in one of these. Peat modules in a similar dehydrated condition, convenient to handle and store, are now available.

Conversely, it is now known that crocks not only fail to assist drainage, they actually impede it, to say nothing of taking up space better occupied by compost.

Another traditional practice was the firming of the compost. The degree of consolidation varied with the subject being grown but for all pots over 130 mm (*5 in*) diameter the compost was forced down with a 'rammer' and good gardeners had a set of rammers for different sizes of pots. It has now been shown that consolidation of the compost is unnecessary and can usually be brought about to the extent required by the subsequent overhead watering of the plant.

Old-fashioned gardening practice also required the use of a large range of pot sizes. The range started with thumbs and thimbles and proceeded by way of small 60s, middle 60s, large 60s, 48s and 32s up to 200 mm (*8 in*), 225 mm (*9 in*) and 250 mm (*10 in*) pots. Plants raised from seed were sown in trays or pans, pricked-out (or pricked-off) into trays and then, according to their vigour, potted (potted-off was the term) into one of the 60s range, i.e. 63 mm (*2½ in*), 75 mm (*3 in*) or 90 mm (*3½ in*) diameter. From this size of pot they might be planted out in the soil or 'potted-on' into larger pots. Potting-on normally required leap-frogging over one size of pot, e.g. from a 75 mm (*3 in*) pot to a 113 mm (*4½ in*) one, or from a 90 mm (*3½ in*) to a 125 mm (*5 in*) one, and so on. Gardeners liked to pot-on at the moment when the plant was beginning to exhaust the nutrient reserves of the compost. When plants were in their 'final' pot they might have to be 'top-dressed' in order to sustain them until ready for sale or display. Top-dressing usually meant scraping away the accumulation of liverwort and moss growing on the surface of the compost, pulling out any weeds and, if their presence was detected, removing any earthworms. This done, fresh compost was put on the surface together with a teaspoonful of an evil-smelling fertiliser containing, among other things, dried blood and steamed bone flour. Liquid feeding was rarely attempted, but when it was, consisted of watering with an infusion made from manure of one kind or another.

All these methods represented a craftsmanship that had been built up over a couple of centuries or more by methods of trial and error, coupled in some cases with beliefs, never questioned, built on misunderstandings. Today economic necessity, coupled with scientific investigation has led to a greatly simplified procedure, outlined here.

Two boxes of seedlings: the one on the right is sown at an acceptable density, and the seedlings are at the correct stage for pricking-off; the box on the left has been sown too thickly, and the seedlings have long since passed the stage at which they should have been pricked-off.

Seed sowing

It is convenient to think of seeds in three simple categories: the small and dust-like, e.g. *Rhododendron, Lobelia*; medium-sized, i.e. seeds which can be seen easily with the naked eye like *Primula* and *Antirrhinum* up to lettuce, *Cyclamen* and tomato, some of which are large enough to be sown singly; and large seeds such as cucumber, melon, sweet pea and so on.

The fine seeds are sown on a compost which has been sieved fairly finely, but not so fine that only the finest particles of the compost go through the sieve producing a material of a silty nature which will set hard on watering. The surface of the compost in the containers must be flat, for which a 'presser' is needed to firm the surface lightly. The seed is then scattered as thinly as possible. Various techniques are used by different people to achieve the fine scattering required, but there is no foolproof method that can be recommended above all others. The scientific approach with fine seeds is to assume that ideally each seedling needs about 1 sq cm in which to expand its cotyledons. Then, allowing for the fact that many of the seeds will not germinate, it is possible to calculate what the sowing rate should be. With dust-like seeds trial and error is all that is possible. Fine seeds do not need to be covered; they must be sown onto a previously watered compost which has drained back to container capacity. Evaporation from the surface, which would hinder germination, is prevented by covering the container with a sheet of glass or polythene and shading with newspaper or cloth to prevent it being overheated by the sunlight.

Medium-sized seeds are sown at rates which seek to provide each with about 3–4 sq cm in which to expand their cotyledons. These are rates which are much easier to calculate and to achieve in practice than those for fine seeds. It is usual to cover them with a scattering of compost sufficient to bury the seed completely to a depth equal to approximately its own diameter. The normal reason for covering a seed is to keep it in an environment uniformly moist, and often to aid the emerging seedling in leaving its seed coat stuck in the compost and in contact with moisture. Glass or plastic covering is still needed to prevent drying out.

Large seeds can be sown in a coarsely sieved compost, say 10 mm (*0.4 in*), and may be best placed in individual containers. This is to some extent a matter of judgement but where germination is fairly reliable individual sowing is usually highly advantageous as it avoids pricking-out, always a serious check to growth. Large seeds in containers can safely be watered from overhead without being dislodged so the practice of covering them with glass or plastic film becomes optional.

Germinating temperatures vary considerably with the subject but 15°C (*60°F*) is suitable for a wide range of hardy and half-hardy plants; 18°C (*65°F*) suits most temperate and sub-tropical plants and 21°C (*70°F*) is required for tropical plants. Maintaining these higher temperatures is difficult without automatic controls, but small propagating cases known as 'propagators' can be used by amateurs to advantage, although they are rather expensive.

Pricking-out is the act of moving a seedling into an individual container or several seedlings into a tray. The time to do it is at the *earliest* possible moment, when the seedling is large enough to be handled, which usually coincides with the expansion of the cotyledons, but before the appearance of true leaves. Careful observation has shown that early pricking-out causes the plant to receive the least amount of check. The older the seedling the greater the amount of root it has, and the more this is damaged in the process the longer the seedling takes to recover from the move.

The container into which the seedling goes depends upon the purpose for which it is to be grown. If it is intended to be a flowering pot-plant it may be pricked-out into a small pot or an intermediate size of container, such as a 'Jiffy' pot. This is a proprietory product which is bought in a dehydrated compressed condition, but after soaking expands into a peat container. For economy of greenhouse space an intermediate size of pot is still necessary while the plant is relatively small; starvation, which was the problem of the gardener of yesterday, can be completely avoided by liquid feeding; but once the plants require more space, and are too large for their containers (top heavy), they are then moved into their final pot.

When plants were transferred to larger pots it was not formerly permitted for them to be watered until several days had elapsed. The theory behind this was that it would give the roots an opportunity to find

Left: paper pots which are glued together in a honeycomb arrangement. Sometimes referred to as Japanese pots from their country of origin, they are extremely useful for raising batches of plants under protection which are intended for subsequent planting out in the garden. *Right:* the paper pots before they have been stretched out to their normal hexagonal shape.

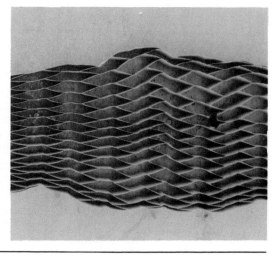

their way into the new compost, which they would not be encouraged to do if they were watered. This strange logic may have had something to do with the excessive firming of the compost which reduced its air-filled porosity. If it was kept on the dry side for a few days it gave the roots an opportunity to grow into it, whereas, if it were watered, such air spaces as it had would be filled with water and new root-growth discouraged. In modern practice, the use of composts with the correct physical conditions and the avoidance of undue compaction should enable watering to be done immediately after potting-on with advantage to the plant.

Seedlings intended ultimately for planting out in the soil may be planted into any of a whole host of biodegradable containers including 'whalehide' pots which are made of special paper, peat pots, fibre pots and possibly best of all peat blocks. For young shrubs, black plastic bags are popular, and old fruit cans once had considerable vogue, so much so that in American nurseries large plastic pots now in general use are still referred to as cans.

In container cultivation, as mentioned elsewhere, a positive choice has to be made between growing plants by the slow-release fertiliser method or by the liquid feeding techniques. Both methods have their advantages and disadvantages but the slow-release fertiliser method wins on the score of simplicity and convenience. Slow-release fertilisers, provided they are used in strict accordance with the makers' recommendations, contain all that the plant requires to sustain it for a period of time. They are all proprietory compounds and it is not possible to give detailed information about them. The compound is mixed thoroughly with the compost before potting takes place. It does not, of course, last for ever and plants which are destined to spend a long life in pots will require ultimately to be liquid-fed.

Liquid feeding will be described specifically in relation to tomatoes and cucumbers, but for general use with pot plants in loam composts the feed is as follows:

Potassium nitrate	72 gram	*11½ oz*
Ammonium nitrate	164 gram	*26 oz*
Water	1 litre	*1 gallon*

This is diluted 200 times (5 ml spoonful/litre; *0.8 fl oz/gallon*) and is given to vigorous plants throughout the year with every watering. Plants which grow more slowly can either have the dilution rate increased to 1 in 400 (5 ml spoonful/2 litres) or alternatively receive the feed at normal strength every other watering.

In loamless composts different factors operate, particularly in hard water areas where the lime content of the compost tends to increase and may cause some plants to suffer from a deficiency of iron and manganese; a condition called lime-induced chlorosis. A recommended mixture is:

Ammonium nitrate	120 gram	*19 oz*
Potassium sulphate	88 gram	*14 oz*
Mono-ammonium phosphate	13 gram	*2 oz*
Water	1 litre	*1 gallon*

The dilution rate, as usual, is 1 : 200 and the recommendations for application are the same as those given for plants in loam composts.

As the range of plants which can be grown in pots is so great and their rates of growth vary so considerably, e.g. a chrysanthemum grows four times as fast as a cyclamen, the amateur has plenty of scope to establish for himself by experience what rate and strength of feeding best suits a particular plant.

When plants are watered from above, the practice is to give sufficient water to fill the space at the top of the pot. The surplus then drains away until the compost is left at container capacity. The faster and more efficiently this happens the better for the healthy functioning of the roots.

Provided the compost has the correct physical properties its air-filled porosity can still be improved if the base-material on which the container is standing has pores of a similar size and range to those of the compost, and sufficient depth to exert drainage pull. There must be no discontinuity between the compost and the base-material and the two must be able to make good contact. Ideally a container should have 25 per cent of its base consisting of holes in order to provide maximum contact between compost and base-material. Many pots and most seed-trays will be seen to be lacking in this respect.

The best material for exerting a drainage pull on the compost is fine sand, the deeper the better, though in practice a depth of 150 mm (*6 in*) is adequate. Coarse sand and gravel drain freely themselves but cannot exert a drainage pull on finer grained materials, the laws of surface tension acting in such a manner as to cause coarse materials to drain freely into less coarse ones and so on, but not the other way round.

Pea-gravel, coarse sand and 6 mm ($\frac{1}{4}$ *in*) granite chippings are frequently used as materials for standing-down beds but are not as effective as is really necessary. A further word of explanation about container capacity might be helpful. When soil in the garden has ceased to drain, i.e. when the force of gravity has pulled down to the water table all the water which the soil could not hold back by surface tension, the soil is said to be at field capacity. This term will not do for containers because the compost they contain is not part of a column of indefinite depth (as is the case with soil) and is not subject to the same drainage pull. This means that container capacity is not only affected by the physical properties of the compost, but also by the height of the container and the drainage properties of the material on which it is standing. The greater the height of the container the better will be its drainage and thus its air-filled porosity. Seed trays, therefore, will be poorly drained compared with 250 mm (*10 in*) pots. This explains why gardeners of an earlier generation insisted on using deep pots called 'long Toms' for plants known to grow in natural soil environments where the air-filled porosity is very high.

Chapter 9

Watering and irrigation systems

This subject is referred to elsewhere in connection with the cultivation of various plants, with the general management of plants in containers and with the management of greenhouses themselves. The subject under discussion here is the actual equipment used.

Horticulturists were very slow to come to the process of watering plants by using sophisticated equipment, preferring for decades to use watering cans and spending countless hours carrying these cans up and down greenhouses. For years the favoured method was to have a tank of water in the house, preferably sunk to ground level, from which cans could be filled rapidly by dipping them into the water. Invariably the water became contaminated with disease and led to endless problems. Watering with hosepipes was regarded with suspicion and was only resorted to for permanently planted crops such as tomatoes and cucumbers or plants in very large pots such as chrysanthemums.

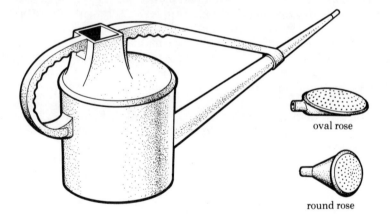

Fig. 18: Haw's pattern watering can of the modern plastic type.

oval rose

round rose

The type of watering can preferred was that known as the 'Haw's Pattern' (it is still available), which is relatively comfortable to carry and comes in many sizes. Larger cans holding two gallons were preferred because they meant less travelling up and down. In general, watering was most often done without a rose on the can so that an individual stream of water could be directed to each plant that was thought to need it.

Watering cans may be fitted with any one of a variety of roses to enable a shower to be delivered instead of a jet: oval roses with small holes are for 'damping down' and for watering seed trays and small pots; oval roses with coarse holes are for watering batches of plants in frames and on staging; round roses are convenient for directing the spray towards one particular pot. An oval rose can be turned around so that the spray is directed

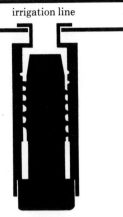

irrigation line

Fig. 19: trickle-irrigation nozzle of the Cameron type. The thread of the barrel is truncated, thus providing a spiral passage for the water.

downwards with its spread reduced or turned upwards to deliver a cascade.

In the world of the commercial grower most of this watering art has gone. The hosepipe with or without a choke, or with a rose fitted to it, has almost replaced the can and whenever possible irrigation systems have replaced both.

Irrigation systems are of three kinds: capillary systems (dealt with elsewhere), trickle systems and spray lines. Trickle systems first appeared in the early 1950s, for watering tomatoes. One of the first was a proprietory system invented by the late Dr Blass and marketed by the then Cameron Irrigation Company. It consisted of lines of thin rubber pipe with nozzles inserted at intervals corresponding with each tomato plant station. The nozzle was most ingenious and consisted of a metal barrel with a truncated thread. Into this was screwed a small bolt, and water escaped along the spiral created by the flattened thread onto the soil surface at rates as slow as one litre (*0.2 gallon*) per hour. The water pressure had to be matched to the number of nozzles and this was achieved by the simple device of fitting a vertical transparent tube to one of the nozzles and adjusting the tap pressure until a column of water rose in the tube to a height of say two metres (*six feet*) which meant the whole system was pressurised to about $23 \, kN/m^2$ (*3 psi*).

With the advent of plastic materials of every sort, trickle irrigation systems are now made by a whole range of manufacturers and the customer can choose whichever seems to suit his purpose best. They are made primarily for watering individual plants, the range now extending from tomatoes in greenhouses through apples and oranges to date palms in the tropics. They can be modified by replacing nozzles with capillary tubes, each of which can supply water to a plant in a pot (the point-watering system); they can be used for irrigating capillary benches; and, finally, they may be so designed that, instead of having nozzles, they seep water along their length, thus moistening bands of soil between rows of plants.

Frequently, displacement-type liquid-feed dilutors (see Fig. 21) are fitted in-line with a trickle irrigation system so that continual liquid

Fig. 20: method of supplying liquid feed to an irrigation system where the flow-rate is too slow to activate the dilutor. When the water level in the tank falls to the level of the lower float switch, the solenoid valve opens to let mains water through fast, activating the dilutor. The tank fills rapidly until the upper float switch closes the solenoid valve.

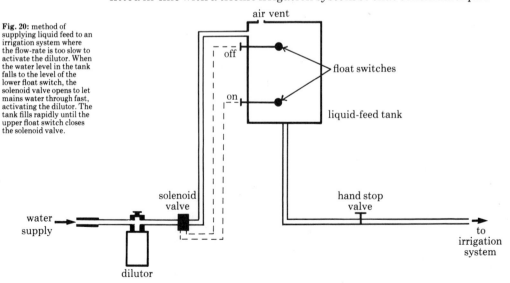

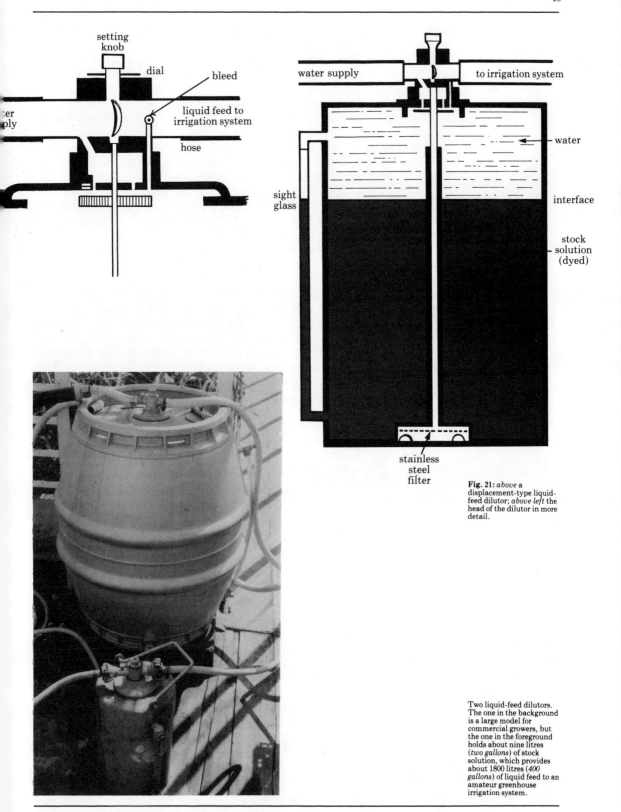

setting
knob

dial

bleed

liquid feed to
irrigation system

hose

ter
ply

water supply

to irrigation system

water

interface

stock
solution
(dyed)

sight
glass

stainless
steel
filter

Fig. 21: *above* a
displacement-type liquid-
feed dilutor; *above left* the
head of the dilutor in more
detail.

Two liquid-feed dilutors.
The one in the background
is a large model for
commercial growers, but
the one in the foreground
holds about nine litres
(*two gallons*) of stock
solution, which provides
about 1800 litres (*400
gallons*) of liquid feed to an
amateur greenhouse
irrigation system.

feeding can take place. For the amateur snags arise here. The first is that the small system he is likely to require will not have a flow-rate sufficient to activate the dilutor, and so he will be forced, if sufficiently enthusiastic, into using a certain amount of gadgetry. This consists of a tank in which two float switches are fixed, one near the top and one near the bottom. From the bottom of the tank a hose connects directly to the irrigation system. This tank must be mounted about $1\frac{1}{2}$ m (*5 ft*) high so that it provides sufficient pressure to activate the system. (See Fig. 20.) As the tank discharges into the irrigation system by gravity the lower float switch will eventually drop and open a solenoid valve. This will allow the tank to be refilled with the water which has passed through the dilutor and so it will, in fact, be liquid feed. When the tank has refilled, the upper float switch will be lifted, and will close the solenoid valve. No garden-scale production could justify this expense, but enthusiasm does not necessarily have to be justified in commercial terms!

The second drawback is that many water authorities will not permit liquid-feed dilutors to be connected directly to the mains water supply.

It is important to understand that when trickle irrigation is used on plants in the soil the water moistens the soil beneath the trickle in the form of an ever-broadening cone. Within this cone of wet soil the roots of the plant will be confined. The more rapidly the cone broadens out, the greater will be the volume of soil available for the roots of that plant. In light sandy soil narrow cones often result, and on such soils it is advisable to spread a 50 mm (*2 in*) thick layer of peat around the plant so that the trickle of water spreads before it percolates downwards. (See Fig. 22.)

If the amateur is unable to incorporate liquid feeding into a trickle-irrigation system, he must rely on the use of slow-release fertilisers for plants in containers, even though this may not give him the precise degree of control of nutrition that might otherwise be desirable.

Spray-lines are normally used for overhead watering and in large houses are suitable for such crops as lettuces. The amateur can use them in the summer for overall watering and for flooding in winter, and if they are of the type which is mounted at low level, they will send sprays of water out horizontally for watering cucumbers and tomatoes. Spray-lines were once very popular in greenhouses but have to some extent been superseded by trickle systems. As they are relatively inexpensive, however, amateurs who use the soil for growing their plants will find them invaluable for winter flooding.

Spray-lines these days are made of rigid plastic pipes and are usually suspended in the house from wire slings. In sunny weather they soften and sag unless supported by a number of slings at one metre (*3 ft*) intervals.

Fig 22: water forms cones of wetted soil below trickle-irrigation nozzles. The relatively narrow cones formed in sandy soils can be broadened if a layer of peat is spread below the nozzle.

trickle irrigation

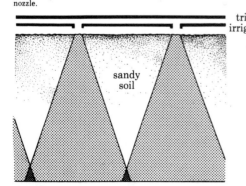

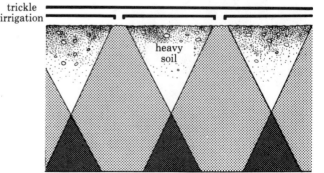

sandy soil

heavy soil

Chapter 10

Greenhouse staging and bench watering

It would seem a simple matter to decide that if you wanted to grow pot plants in a greenhouse and have them at a height at which it was convenient both to see and work with them, you could construct an elevated platform on which to stand them. Like many other things in horticulture it is not as simple as it might appear.

Solid and open staging

To begin with, the position of the bench, or staging as it is properly called, is very important because of the flow of convection currents in the house. In general the warm air from the heating pipes or heater rises up to the ridge of the house, and as it loses heat it sinks alongside the under surface of the roof. Should the staging go right to the wall of the house and be joined to it the cooled air will spread across the staging thus bringing about a temperature lower than the average for the house. The mean temperature of the greenhouse atmosphere is usually referred to as the ambient temperature. This name is important because it distinguishes it from the temperature of any surface within the house which is receiving radiant heat from the sun and which may well have a temperature above the ambient.

To return to the staging: it should always be fixed so that a gap of at least 150 mm (*6 in*) is left between it and the wall of the house through which the heavier cool air can flow downwards to be reheated.

By the same token it follows that if the staging consists of welded mesh wire or wooden slats, cooled air will also sink through it to be rewarmed by the pipes below. This will ensure that the temperature on the bench is closer to the ambient. For all winter work and when a warm temperature around the plants in the staging is required it is always recommended that 'open staging' be provided. In summer, on the other hand, open benches can lead to arid conditions around the pots, to the extent that some growers actually install overhead spray-lines so that they can spray the plants from time to time in order to make them moister and thus cooler.

It has been traditional for gardeners to construct solid benches with a floor of flat asbestos sheeting, or for greater strength, corrugated asbestos or galvanised iron. The staging has then been covered with one of a variety of materials such as sand, pea gravel, granulated peat, or sifted clinker. It is only recently, as mentioned earlier, that the advantages of fine sand have become apparent.

Solid staging, whether bare or covered with one of the materials mentioned is, if dry, hot in the day because of the radiation it receives from the sun, and conversely very cool at night because of the radiation it emits. If the covering material is wet a cool environment is provided around the pots and containers standing on it because of evaporative cooling. When water evaporates from a surface, the heat required to change it from liquid to vapour is taken from the surface concerned. On a solid staging covered with a water-retaining medium like those mentioned above, evaporation

Two kinds of staging. In the foreground is open staging made from galvanised mild steel welded mesh, and in the background solid staging on which corrugated asbestos has been covered with a coarse grit sand (fine sand would have been better).

takes place all the time, also from the surface of the compost in the pots and other containers, and finally from the leaves of the plants themselves by means of the evaporative process botanists call transpiration. The cumulative effect of all this, plus the fact that the cooled air has to flow over the side of the staging instead of through it, explains why the solid stage can be a much cooler place than the open one. In winter it may be very disadvantageous, but in summer it is quite the reverse for many plants.

The height and width of staging is a subject to which pot-plant growers have devoted a lot of attention, but the amateur usually has little room for manoeuvre. He has really only two alternatives: the first, to build a central stage to be reached from either side, an arrangement likely to provide considerable access problems in a small greenhouse; the second, to construct a stage on one or both sides of the central path. A double stage should not exceed about 1800 mm (*6 ft*) in width and a single stage should not exceed 900 mm (*3 ft*). These widths should allow all parts of the bench to be reached easily by anybody of average height. The lower the bench the greater the reach permitted but the more the back has to be bent; and the higher it is the more it will be reduced by the slope of the roof. A height of 835–900 mm (*33–36 in*) is thought to be the most comfortable and convenient for most people. In a small greenhouse height is often determined by the height of the side walls, because if the staging comes above the wall, space will be lost due to the incline of the roof. It is also best for even circulation of heat if the heating pipes can be mounted on the walls of the house rather than under the staging. When staging is properly installed the plants on it tend to dry evenly because the temperature across it is even.

Bench watering

As methods of irrigating plants in pots in the greenhouse are affected by the type of staging, the two should be considered together. Irrigation methods are of two kinds: first, the capillary bench where water rises up into the pot through the force of capillary attraction; second, the point-watering system where a main supply pipe has small capillary tubes conducting water from it to the surface of the compost in each pot. This is sometimes referred to as the 'spaghetti system'. The narrowness of the internal diameter of the tubes causes the water flow to be reduced to a trickle.

Open staging on which a multi-point watering system is installed for watering individual pots such as the dwarf chrysanthemums depicted.

Capillary systems, though all working on the same principle, are many and varied. First to be developed were the sand benches, which divide into two types. In the more simple type the bench is covered with a sheet of plastic film and then 50 mm (*2 in*) of fairly fine sand. A trickle irrigation system is then laid over the sand which is wetted until water is dripping out from the edges of the sand. The sand has to be wetted frequently enough to keep it fully charged with water at all times and thus to prevent it drying sufficiently for the roots of the plants to grow out of the pots and root through into the sand. When the pots are removed such plants suffer a check in growth, possibly a severe one. This correct irrigation is very difficult to bring about in practice, and it is only recently that a device has been made available which monitors the wetness of the sand and is able to activate a circuit which will open a valve to let water into the irrigation system.

Not only is sand heavy, but it tends to become covered with algae, and is now often replaced by mats made of plastic fibres which are lightweight

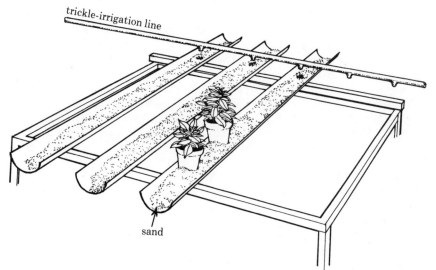

trickle-irrigation line

sand

Fig. 23: a staging consisting of lengths of guttering filled with sand, between which cold air can sink. The lengths of guttering slope slightly down from the trickle-irrigation line, which can be left on all the time.

and more convenient. There are different kinds available, but none has the capillary properties of fine sand, which is twice as good as the best of them.

Another development of the sand capillary bed was to make it fully automatic by waterproofing the staging completely with plastic film and then introducing water into the sand by means of a plastic pipe running along the centre of the bench below the sand. Perforations in the pipe every few centimetres allow water to seep into the sand to saturate it to a level just below its surface. This is carefully controlled by a float valve in a header tank which receives the water supply. A proprietory version of this 'do-it-yourself system' has the water level controlled by a device similar to a carburettor float chamber. The fully automatic sand bench (now adaptable to capillary matting) offers many attractions to the amateur, particularly in the summer time.

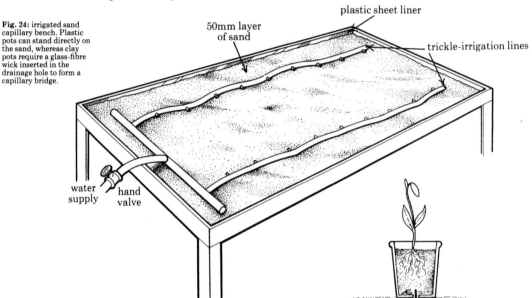

Fig. 24: irrigated sand capillary bench. Plastic pots can stand directly on the sand, whereas clay pots require a glass-fibre wick inserted in the drainage hole to form a capillary bridge.

plastic sheet liner

50mm layer of sand

trickle-irrigation lines

water supply

hand valve

wick

Another variation which attempts to combine the advantages of the capillary bench with those of the open bench is to construct a framework which supports parallel lengths of asbestos cement guttering filled with fine sand. The sand is wetted by a trickle irrigation system and the spaces between the lengths of gutter allow cool air to sink past the plants.

One notable disadvantage with capillary bench irrigation systems is the difficulty of liquid feeding the pot plants without introducing a liquid-feed dilutor into the irrigation system, which would be expensive for the amateur. With fully automatic sand capillary benches, the flow of water to the bench is insufficient to activate a liquid-feed dilutor and complicated arrangements are needed to overcome this drawback.

When we turn to point-watering systems we find that we are confined to using them for larger pots, because there are not sufficient capillary tubes available on a harness for a batch of small pots standing close together. Another limitation is that if the pots on a staging are of different sizes they will all require different amounts of water to bring them to container capacity. This may necessitate taking two capillary tubes to a larger pot so that it receives, in the same time, twice as much water as a smaller one.

Unfortunately this simple expedient does not stop smaller pots drying more rapidly than larger ones. Watering may have to be done so that the larger pots get enough and the smaller ones get too much; not a matter for concern in the summer, but undesirable in the winter.

It is difficult to reconcile all the conflicting facts about staging in greenhouses, related systems of irrigation, and the materials with which staging is covered. The facts are:

1 Staging must be so arranged that it does not collect cold air.
2 Open staging provides a warmer and drier environment than solid staging – good in winter but perhaps too dry in the summer. It can be combined only with point-watering systems. It does not provide any assistance in draining pots and therefore militates against good air-filled porosity. This does not matter greatly if composts have excellent physical condition with air-filled porosity over 15 per cent, or in summer when evaporation is rapid.
3 Solid staging, provided it is covered with fine sand which is kept wet, gives a cool and moist environment. It can be exploited for capillary irrigation in the summer if it is given a water-table just below its surface. In winter if the sand is 150 mm (6 in) deep it will effectively drain containers and assist in maintaining good air-filled porosity at a time when evaporation rates are low.
4 All other materials which are used for covering staging have poor drainage pulling qualities in comparison with fine sand.
5 Benches carrying a 150 mm (6 in) depth of sand need to be very robust and are expensive to construct and equip.
6 Fine sand, if kept moist, rapidly becomes colonised by green algae. This can be controlled by the use of algicides.
7 To overcome the cooler environment of a solid bench the greenhouse heating-system thermostat should be installed just a little above the bench.

Chapter 11

Cold frames

Frames have been in use for as long as greenhouses, providing for them a most important ancillary function. In fact it is difficult properly to utilise a greenhouse, heated or cold, without the back-up a frame provides. Some qualification is required because cold-frames are used for a number of purposes such as producing early vegetables, raising the seeds of vegetables and flowers, and striking cuttings of shrubs and herbaceous perennials.

The cold-frame associated with the greenhouse is used for holding plants in containers until they are either moved out into the open or returned back to the greenhouse. Traditionally the greenhouse cold-frame has always had an ash base over clinker, but modern studies of water movements in pots and other containers require a re-appraisal of this practice. The cold-frame is being discussed for the simple reason that heated frames are an expensive luxury which few can afford, although they do add a further dimension to greenhouse growing.

Frames can be constructed from various materials, of which brick is best, but timber the more common. Whatever the material, the frame, these days, is best covered with Dutch lights: first because they are the cheapest, and second, because they admit more light into the frame than any other kind. The Dutch light consists of a wooden frame measuring 1500 mm × 780 mm (*4 ft 11 in × 31 in*) (some manufacturers make a Dutch light 810 mm wide (*32 in*)) into which a single sheet of glass 1420 mm × 730 mm (*56 in × 29 in*) is slid and is secured top and bottom by wooden cleats

Fig. 26: non-reversible Dutch light. The dimensions shown are the precise British standard.

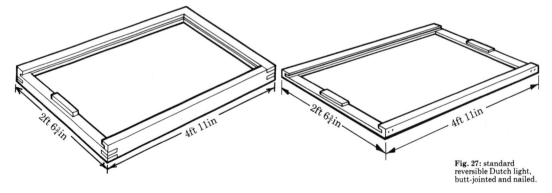

Fig. 27: standard reversible Dutch light, butt-jointed and nailed.

fixed with galvanised nails. The standard reversible Dutch light is butt-jointed and nailed, but, at slightly more cost, versions are available with comb and feather joints, glued together with waterproof glue, and with the top rail grooved so that the glass is supported in grooves along three of its sides. The standard reversible light is adequate for most purposes.

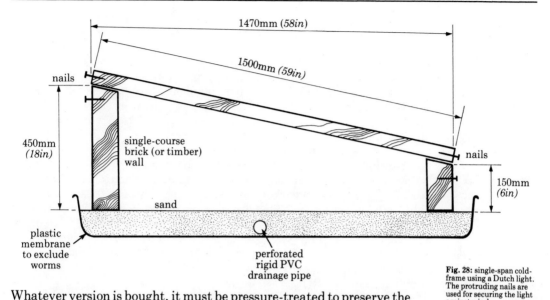

Fig. 28: single-span cold-frame using a Dutch light. The protruding nails are used for securing the light against wind.

Whatever version is bought, it must be pressure-treated to preserve the wood (see page 18).

When using Dutch lights it is possible to construct either a single frame or a span frame. A single frame consists of a high back wall and a lower front one. The exact height of each is a matter of convenience related to the size of plant to be accommodated. One reasonable arrangement is a back wall 450 mm (*18 in*) high and a front one 150 mm (*6 in*) high giving a fall of 300 mm (*12 in*). Such a frame would have an overall width of 1470 mm (*58 in*) (see Fig. 28).

A span frame is more economical and convenient with regard to utilisation of space. It is also cheaper to construct per area covered; but cannot, of course, be built as a lean-to structure against the greenhouse. It consists of a ridge board 100 mm (*4 in*) wide and 25 mm (*1 in*) thick supported on uprights driven into the ground at one metre (*3 ft*) intervals. Nailed along the centre of the ridge board and on its upper face is a ridge-fin 25 mm × 25 mm (*1 in × 1 in*). The two side walls should not be less than 150 mm (*6 in*) high with the ridge 550 mm (*22 in*) high. Such a frame would be 2700 mm (*9 ft*) wide overall. If the side walls are required to be higher the ridge should be raised by an equal amount. If timber is used for construction it should, for preference, be pressure-treated, otherwise painted liberally with a copper preservative such as Cuprinol. (See Fig. 29.)

The frame, single or span, obviously can be of any length, but if it can be about the same as that of the greenhouse it accompanies, it will normally be adequate.

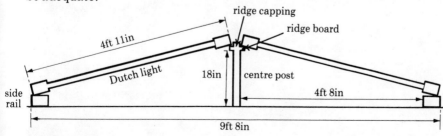

Fig. 29: double Dutch-light span frame.

A careful experiment at Stockbridge House Experimental Horticulture Station, Cawood, Yorkshire, in the early 1950s, showed surprisingly little difference in the winter growth of lettuces in span frames orientated in various directions. This being the case, a frame can be placed in the garden in the most convenient position, provided, of course, that it is not in the shadow of buildings or screens. A popular idea in the past was to construct a frame as a lean-to on either side of a north–south greenhouse or on the south side of an east–west one. This is a satisfactory arrangement with houses that have base walls of sufficient height.

Frames made from Dutch lights are not elaborate structures and the methods for securing the lights against wind are simple. Lights on single frames have a nail driven halfway into the middle of each end rail and two others similarly into each wall in a position directly below those in the light. Galvanised wire wrapped around each pair of nails will hold the light down. With span frames, nails are driven halfway into the upper surface of one end rail of each light and halfway into the edge of the other end rail of each. When the lights are placed on the frame each pair is hinged together with wire wrapped around the nails protruding upwards from the end rails

Fig. 30: fixing Dutch lights on frames to secure them against wind.

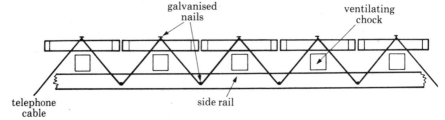

and across the ridge. (See Fig. 30.) They are secured at their lower ends to the side walls in exactly the same way as with single frames.

One of the great advantages of cold-frames is the facility they provide for giving plants increasing ventilation until they can withstand full exposure to the normal climate – the process known as hardening-off. Lights are propped up with wooden chocks to provide ventilation: a piece of wood measuring 50 mm × 100 mm × 150 mm (*2 in × 4 in × 6 in*) will provide three positions. If greater ventilation is required than this chock provides, then the time has come when the light can be removed altogether during the daytime. Dutch lights can easily be lifted by one person and when removed must be carefully stacked and secured.

A single-span Dutch-light frame being used for hardening-off bedding plants in an amateur's garden. The frame in the middle is covered with a plastic-mesh shading material which can also be used in frosty weather to provide further protection.

In winter time, protection extra to that provided by the glass may be needed, for which purpose the frame is covered with heavy-grade hessian fabric. At one time reed mats were made specifically for the purpose of covering frames. These, like hessian, are now difficult to obtain. The plastic fabrics used for thermal screens might provide a modern substitute.

Plants being hardened-off in frames are sometimes in danger of being scorched during periods of bright spring and early summer sunshine. To prevent this the glass of the light is sprayed with a shading material. This must be washed off before the lights are brought back into service in the autumn.

As previously stated, it was the practice to remove the soil to a depth of 150 mm (*6 in*) or so, put down a bed of clinker and cover this with ash to form a base on which the various containers could stand. The 'standing-base' for containers, as it is now called, has been shown to be almost as important as the compost in which the plants are growing. It has the function in summer of supplying water to the containers by capillarity and distributing it evenly over the whole standing area. In winter it has the function of draining the compost in the containers to maintain its air-filled porosity.

Nurserymen are being recommended to construct special standing-bases or standing-down beds for their container-grown plants. This bed was designed at the Experimental Horticulture Station of the Ministry of Agriculture, Fisheries and Food at Efford in Hampshire.

The bed is made of fine lime-free sand at least 50 mm (*2 in*) deep, and preferably 150 mm (*6 in*). It is lined with 500 gauge black polythene which is brought over the retaining walls and ends. A perforated 25 mm (*1 in*) alkathene pipe runs along the bed, under the sand, to act as a drainage channel to remove all surplus water to a soak-away.

Plants in containers standing on a base material which is provided with a capillary watering system. The wire hoops are for placing polythene film over the area, either for protection from weather or to provide a propagation environment.

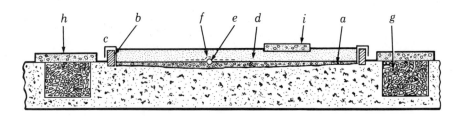

Fig. 31: a drained sand
bed adapted to form a
standing-base for a
cold-frame.

a   levelling sand or shingle
b   timber side boards
c   500g black polythene enclosing bed
d   firmed, clean, sharp sand (50mm depth)
e   25mm plastic pipe with 5mm drainage holes
f   porous material to prevent pipe silting up
g   soakaway trench
h   outer pathway slab
i   access pathway (if required)

There is no reason why such a bed could not be adapted to provide the base for a cold frame. (See Fig. 31.) A frame is, after all, no more than a standing-down bed, with removable glass cover.

Hardening-off has already been described as a process of acclimatisation from one environment to another, for which the cold-frame is particularly suitable, but it may be helpful to enlarge a little more upon it. If plants are suddenly subjected to a change of environment which involves a lowering of temperature and exposure to a much more turbulent atmosphere, the soft tissue they will have developed previously will suffer considerable damage before their natural powers of adaptability have had time to bring about the necessary changes. Plants can often survive within quite a wide temperature band, but grow at different rates at either end of it, producing softer tissues at the higher end and harder ones at the lower end. The hardening-off process in frames is a procedure for bringing about these temperature-induced changes gradually in a situation sheltered from atmospheric turbulence, where protection from sudden extremes of temperature is also available. Meanwhile the environment outside the frame is gradually improving. After a few weeks the adaptation of the plant and the improvement in its intended environment have reached the point of coincidence, where acclimatisation has been achieved.

Chapter 12

Pests and diseases

Green plants directly and indirectly provide the food for most other living things including, of course, man. When other living things are in direct competition with man for a particular plant or crop they are referred to as pests, diseases, parasites and the like. Technically any life form attacking a plant is, in plain language, a pest and in scientific language a pathogen, and causes the plant to be diseased. For convenience horticulturists categorise pathogens into *pests* which are invertebrate animals, mostly insects and mites, and *diseases*, which are caused by fungi, bacteria and viruses. In addition plants may be in a state of ill-health without any pathogen being responsible. Such conditions are referred to as physiological disorders, and are caused by an abnormality in the environment, e.g. waterlogging, nutrient deficiency, chemical damage etc. Finally, vermin such as mice, squirrels and rabbits may cause havoc. No one would hesitate to call them pests, though strictly speaking they are vertebrate animals as opposed to the more common invertebrates.

Plants under glass may be diseased through any of the preceding causes, some of which attack anything whereas others are more selective in their choice of host. The subject of pests and diseases and their control is the source of an abundant literature, some of which is very academic. In Great Britain the Ministry of Agriculture, Fisheries and Food (MAFF) produces

The red spider mite, which is a serious and common pest of plants in greenhouses, particularly heated greenhouses. It is almost impossible to avoid attacks from this pest sooner or later, and pesticides have to be used to control it. (The biological control by means of a parasite used by commercial growers is impracticable for amateurs.)

annually a book entitled *Approved Products for Farmers and Growers* which is regarded as a standard work of reference and which lists all the products approved for general use in agriculture and horticulture; it gives the name of each pesticide by which it is internationally known; the purposes for which it may be effectively used; the limitations to its use, e.g. plants which are damaged by it, if any; pests which may develop resistance to it and any hazards attendant upon its use together with the precautions which should be adopted; it then lists the manufacturers and the proprietory names under which they sell it. In another section it gives information on the pests and diseases of various important plants and the chemicals which control them. It is well worth the cost, and in spite of the new products which continue to come onto the market, one edition remains sufficiently up-to-date for two or three years.

Should the gardener use the above book he can find which chemicals are available for use for a specific problem, but he will not know whether the product is available in suitable small packs. To guide him through this difficulty the MAFF produces another very useful publication entitled *Chemicals for the Gardener*. This lists the chemicals available for the amateur and gives brief but accurate information on the identification of the more common pests and diseases. Lastly the MAFF also produces a series of *Advisory Leaflets*, each on a specific pest or disease; they are continually updated and give the best advice available on the subject at a very modest cost. A catalogue is published annually by Her Majesty's Stationery Office listing, with their prices, all the publications available. Another source of information is to be found in the booklets produced by the pesticide firms, which often contain a vast amount of technical information in condensed and tabulated form.

Application of pesticides

Pesticide chemicals can be applied in greenhouses in a number of different ways. The most familiar method is high-volume spraying which is where the chemical is dissolved in a large amount of water and then applied as a drenching spray all over the crop. Next and equally familiar is fumigation which is when a chemical is vaporised in the greenhouse, usually by heat. Fumigation has to some extent been superseded by the use of smokes

A plastic walk-in tunnel being fumigated by means of a smoke.

which are pyrotechnic devices on which a fuse is lit to produce dense smoke which carries particles of the chemical to all parts of the house. Aerosols work on a similar principle. It is now possible to purchase electric devices whereby a very low-volume spray is distributed so that minute droplets of the fluid reach all parts of the plant. The last method, and the least popular, is dusting.

It is difficult to say which is the best method of application because it depends on the problem that is being dealt with, the size of the house and so on, but a light plastic pneumatic sprayer or similar hand-operated knapsack sprayer is really indispensable for the application of high-volume sprays. If the substance to be applied can be obtained as a smoke or aerosol, so much the better, and if an electric atomiser can be afforded then the armoury will be quite formidable.

All parts of the plant are susceptible to attack by pathogens, the roots as much as the aerial parts. Soil-borne pathogens have already been mentioned in Chapter 6 as well as their eradication by heat sterilisation by means of steam. This remains an extremely effective way of dealing with them and, although it cannot penetrate deeply enough to deal completely with tomato mosaic virus or certain wilt-causing fungi, nothing has superseded it. Notwithstanding this, in the last few years effective chemical sterilants have been developed for disinfecting the greenhouse soil, the compost for containers and even the soil round individual plants in the greenhouse. The more important of these are:

Pesticides

Metham-sodium. This can be purchased as a liquid preparation under the names of 'Vapam' or 'Sistan' or as a solid prilled* material under the name of 'Dazomet'. It is used as a chemical sterilant for the greenhouse soil or for sterilising compost loam. After application the soil has to be covered with a plastic sheet to stop the methyl isothiocyanate vapour it gives off escaping. After three weeks of fumigation the soil is uncovered and cultivated three times at fortnightly intervals to rid it of residual fumes which are phytotoxic (injurious to plant tissues).

* see Glossary

Drazoxolon. This is a fungicide sold under the name of 'Milcol' and is used against the damping-off disease of seedlings (*Pythium debarryanum*). Containers ready for sowing can be treated before the seed is sown (or afterwards if there is no danger of the seed being washed away) and also when the seedlings have been pricked-off.

Etridiazole. This is available under the trade names 'Truban', 'Terrazole' and 'Aaterra'. It is effective against the damping-off disease of seedlings and footrot *(Phytophthora* species) and is now very widely used for this purpose.

Cheshunt Compound. This mixture has been in use for over fifty years and is very effective against the damping-off disease of seedlings.

New materials or mixtures of existing ones with a broader spectrum of activity are being developed or are under trial.

The common pests of greenhouse crops, the appearance of which sooner or later is inevitable, are aphids, known as greenfly (although they may be all sorts of other colours), red spider and whitefly. All are very difficult to control because of their ability to develop resistant strains to new pesticides. As it is impossible to give specific recommendations for the control of the first two, you should purchase two or three different pesticides recommended for the control of each of these pests and use them in turn. For red spider and whitefly commercial growers of tomatoes and cucumbers use 'integrated control', which is a careful blend of chemical and biological control. Unfortunately it is quite beyond the resources of the amateur.

Biological control means the introduction of a parasite which will reduce the population of the pest to a point where its effect can be tolerated. It was thought at one time that it would prove the answer to the problem for amateur and professional alike, but in the event it proved impossible to maintain the parasite population in small greenhouses.

A fairly recently developed group of pesticides (e.g. Resmethrin) is that known as the synthetic pyrethroids. These are proving very successful against whitefly, and are now available in small packs for amateur gardeners.

Since the advent of peat composts and capillary beds, sciarid fly or fungus gnat has become a serious pest of plants in containers. The small flies are seen on the surface of the compost but the damage is caused by the maggots which feed on the roots of the plants. A sharp look out should be kept for this pest and if it is seen Diazinon should be used as a drench.

Another general pest of pot plants is the tarsonemid mite, sometimes called the cyclamen mite. It is waxy white or light brown in colour and hardly visible to the naked eye. The leaves of pot plants are attacked and become brittle and curled. Their surfaces may become purple and dark with a cracked appearance. An effective control is to spray the plants with dicofol (sold under the trade name of Kelthane).

Fungicides

Turning to fungal diseases, we have as general troublemakers the powdery mildews. There are many different species concerned, but the symptoms of their damage are white spores which look like powder and which cover the leaves and stems of the host plant. Benomyl (sold as Benlate) has proved very effective against the powdery mildews. It is a systemic fungicide and can be used as a root drench as well as a spray. It has prophylactic effects as well as curative ones. It is effective against many other fungal diseases in addition to the powdery mildews. Incidentally, powdery mildews are active in dry conditions whereas the downy mildews as a general rule require very damp and moist environments. The dreaded tomato leaf mould (*Cladosporium fulvum*) is similar to the powdery mildews, but brown in colour, and is also controlled by Benlate.

The downy mildews which attack grapes, lettuce and some pot plants have to be controlled by protective sprays based on copper compounds, sold under such trade names as Colloiclox, Fungex, Cuprokylt and Perenox. Such sprays are most effective if applied before the disease appears and in anticipation that it will do so. Do not delay until symptoms appear. The dithiocarbarmate group, of which zineb is most readily available to the amateur, is effective against downy mildews as well as other diseases.

Perhaps the most common fungus seen under glass is the grey mould fungus (*Botrytis cinerea*). Normally it does not attack healthy tissues but confines itself to dead plant tissue on which it forms the common, ever present, grey fluff of decay. It can, however, pass from dead or dying tissue into living tissue; if, for example, tomatoes are de-leafed so that stumps are left on the stem to die, *Botrytis* can establish itself on them and then pass into the stem and kill the plant. If this is seen to be happening and can

Cucumber leaves which have been badly affected by powdery mildew.

be taken in time, a dab of creosote on the lesion will save the plant. A dab means a very small amount – if the creosote is put all round the stem the plant will die. *Botrytis* attacks tomato fruits where they are attached to the stalk causing them to fall to the ground. In cold greenhouses it also causes spots to form on the fruits. Strawberry fruits are sometimes attacked, but spraying with Benomyl or Captan will give good control.

Virus diseases

Virus diseases attack most plants grown under glass. The two most common viruses are tomato mosaic virus (TMV), originally called tobacco mosaic virus, and cucumber yellow mottle mosaic. The latter has a very wide range of hosts. A number of viruses attack chrysanthemums and carnations, and, in fact, it is difficult to find any plant of importance which does not have some virus enemy. Viruses are spread mainly by sap-sucking insects, among which winged aphids are by far the most important, so that aphid control is an indirect method of virus control. Viruses rarely kill their host, but they weaken it and may make it unsightly and perhaps unusable. The most common symptom is mosaicing of the leaves, sometimes distortion of the leaf or flower, and a characteristic spotting called Ringspot. Virus diseases can be eradicated from stocks of plants by special propagation techniques known as meristem culture or micro-propagation (see Appendix VII). The principle underlying this practice is to propagate the plant from a few cells excised from the growing tip of a stem before the virus particles have had time to enter them. This method has provided us with virus-free stocks of many plants, particularly carnations and chrysanthemums.

Physiological disorders

The tomato provides a number of examples of physiological disorders. Blossom end rot is one that plagues amateur gardeners. It is characterised by a dark brown hard sunken lesion at the point of the fruit where the petals were originally attached. It is thought to be caused by the plant having undergone water stress coupled with calcium deficiency at some time. Plants in peat modules are very susceptible if the modules are not watered frequently enough. Blotchy ripening and greenback of the fruits are other physiological disorders with rather more complicated causes; magnesium deficiency is due to potassium levels in the soil being too high in relation to magnesium. Shanking of grapes (see page 100) is a physiological disorder, probably connected with moisture stress in the plant, and so probably is tipburn of lettuces which is a constant anxiety to the commercial grower.

The avoidance of physiological disorders is simple in theory, because all that is required is to ensure that there are no imbalancing factors in the plant's environment. In practice every experienced grower knows that the more sophisticated the cultivation of a crop the greater becomes the risk of physiological disorders occurring.

For further information on pesticides see Appendix III.

Chapter 13

Varieties and cultivars

All the vegetables, fruits and flowers whose cultivation under glass is described in these pages may be had in slightly different versions. These were formerly called varieties because they vary from each other. In modern botanical language they are called cultivars (or c.v. for short) which is a contraction and joining of the term 'cultivated variety'. The term 'variety' is now used by botanists with a specific non-horticultural meaning.

It must be understood that all plants raised from seed within a particular species are individuals in their own right. As such they vary, albeit slightly, from each other and are, therefore, varieties. If one such variant is selected and multiplied by the gardener it automatically becomes a cultivar.

As usual, matters in horticulture are not quite as straightforward as this, because some awkward questions immediately arise. If every seedling is a unique individual, how is it possible to raise an invariant cultivar from seed? The answer is, that it is not really possible, except in some cases where it almost is.

Most plants, but not all, have fairly elaborate mechanisms to ensure that they are not self-pollinated. Hence almost all of the seedlings that arise will have had two distinct parents – a factor which of itself will result in variation and confer greater survival potential on the species. With such plants the breeder and seedsman has to rely in normal circumstances on selecting plants for seed production which are very similar, in the hope that they will produce seedlings with a high degree of uniformity. This method, called mass selection, has been in use for a long time and has served us very well, although not perfectly.

There are, on the other hand, a minority of plants, including the tomato and cucumber, which are quite happy to accept self-pollination. The tomato, in fact, self-pollinates naturally, and tends to breed very true to type. Thus a cultivar such as 'Ailsa Craig' is very stable, and it is possible to have seed from it for many generations, without much change taking place.

F1 hybrids

In recent times, plant breeders have gone beyond the role of marriage broker to the point of master-minding the plant's private act of procreation: the F1 hybrid has been the consequence. It is possible by various means to self-pollinate most plants, however elaborate the mechanism they have developed to prevent it. 'Selfing' results in a segregation of characteristics in the progeny. Those having a full share of the desired ones can be selected, and those with a preponderance of the undesirable ones discarded. A repetition of the process will further intensify the sought-after characteristics.

This is fine, and would suffice were it not for the fact that 'selfed' plants progressively lose vigour, including yield. If, however, these selfed and highly uniform selections (pure lines as they are called) are crossed with others, unrelated but similarly produced, the resulting progeny, the first crosses or first hybrids, will almost certainly regain all the lost vigour and more, as well as resulting in a highly desirable cultivar. This, in outline, is how F1 hybrids are produced: F1 stands for the first filial generation. If the F1 hybrids are used as parents there will be a seemingly random distribution of characteristics among the progeny and the advantages of uniformity will be lost, so it is pointless to save the seed for using next year. The availability of F1 hybrids lies in the production and maintenance of the pure lines which constitute their parents. F1 hybrid seed is very expensive in comparison with ordinary seed, but its advantages usually outweigh this many times.

Clones

When one is dealing with perennial plants such as peaches and vines it is possible to maintain a cultivar for a very long time by means of vegetative propagation (see Chapter 30). It means that every plant of the 'Black Hamboro' grape is a piece, as it were, of the original plant. A cultivar of this kind is called a clone and there is no reason why it should not go on forever; at least in theory. In practice clones have often degenerated due to viral disease, and only in very recent times has it been possible to rid them of these diseases and to restore them to what presumably was their original condition.

Available cultivars

The following lists mention various cultivars, both old and new, with brief comments. Gardeners should experiment with different cultivars and not become wedded irrevocably to one with which, in the past, they have been successful, because better ones may exist. However, it must be remembered that although many cultivars are introduced in the seed catalogues every year many are 'here today and gone tomorrow'.

Tomatoes

The old favourites are:

Ailsa Craig	They are still available. They are long-jointed and
Harbinger	make tall plants. Fruit quality is excellent.
Moneymaker	'Moneymaker' is less liable to greenback than the others. All are susceptible to tomato leaf mould and to TMV.

Some well-established F1 varieties are:

Eurocross BB	Both are resistant to leaf mould, but not TMV, and
Amberley Cross	ripen well without greenback. They perform better in heated houses but because of their resistance to disease are very attractive.

Two very modern F1 hybrids are:

Sonatine	This is resistant to TMV, five races of leaf mould and two races of fusarium wilt.
Sonato	This is resistant to TMV, two races of leaf mould and one race of fusarium wilt.
	Both are small-fruited varieties and are bred for high-temperature production.

Cucumbers

The old favourites are:

Telegraph	A long smooth cucumber.
Butcher's Disease Resister	A spiny type.

A well-established F1 variety is:

Sporu	It is of the spiny type and resistant to leaf-spot disease and gummosis.

Two popular modern F1 hybrids are:

Farbio Fabiola	Both have only female flowers, and are resistant to gummosis and leaf spot. They are sometimes obtainable as chitted seed so that the gardener can avoid the difficulty of providing them with the high germination temperature they require.

Female cucumber flower. The embryo cucumber lies behind the flower, which must not be fertilised.

Melon The musk or netted types:
King George (scarlet flesh)
Hero of Lockinge (white flesh)

The cantaloups:
Charantais
Sweetheart (F1)
Ogen
Tiger

Sweet Pepper

Bellboy	F1 hybrid and probably the most popular variety.
Sweet Westland	Also called 'Danube'.
New Ace	F1 hybrid with an award of merit from the Royal Horticultural Society's trials.

Aubergine Most of the modern varieties are F1 hybrids such as:
Aubrina
Moneymaker
Dobrix

Lettuce For cold-house production the old favourite is 'May Queen' which is still available from seedsmen. Others more recently introduced are 'Kwiek', 'Kloek' and 'Delta'.
  For heated houses special varieties have been produced, such as:
Dandie
Wintosa
Baldina
Ostinata
The wide range of lettuce cultivars we now have for greenhouse production did not exist ten years ago. It has come about through intensive breeding programmes both in Holland and at the Glasshouse Crops Research Institute in Sussex, England.

French Beans Dwarf cultivars include:

The Prince	The best-known.
Masterpiece	A close runner-up to 'The Prince'.
Rolando	A stringless* variety grown extensively under glass; cylindrical in shape and about 130 mm ($5\frac{1}{2}$ in) long.

*Stringless means that there are no fibres either side of the pod which have to be pared away before cooking. It does not mean that they do not have to be grown up strings.

Climbing cultivars include:

Blue Lake	The standard cultivar for growing under glass.
Green Streamer	
Bergon	A stringless variety.
Phenomenon	

Potatoes For greenhouse cultivation early cultivars must be used. The best known are:
Arran Pilot
Home Guard
Sharpe's Express

Figs For people living in this country it is tempting to think that a fig is just a fig. In fact there are several cultivars. Some were grown fifty to a hundred

years ago, and may still be available. They are:
Brown Turkey
White Ischia
White Marseilles

In the high days of private gardening a whole selection of grape cultivars **Grapes**
was available. Many of them today are difficult to come by, but some
nurserymen may offer stocks.
Sweet water or early types include:
Black Hamboro   A black grape, thought by some to be the grape *par excellence.*
Foster's Seedling A white grape.

Mid-season cultivars:
Muscat of Alexandria
Madresfield Court

The vinous or late types:
Black Alicante
Gros Colmar

The difference between peaches and nectarines is only skin deep, the **Peaches and**
peach having a rough skin and the nectarine a smooth one more like a **nectarines**
plum. Nectarines are in many ways preferable to peaches, but for a time
dropped from favour. They are now enjoying something of a revival. As
with grapes, fifty years ago there were many varieties obtainable. Today
very few are offered for sale.

Peaches – the best known are:
Hale's Early
Duke of York
Peregrine

Nectarines:
Cardinal
Early Rivers
Lord Napier

The early cultivars used for forcing are common in Yorkshire, but rare in **Rhubarb**
other parts of Britain. They are:
Timperley Early   'Timperley Early' and 'Gillings Red' are probably identical.
Gillings Red
Royal Prince Albert
Victoria
Other varieties of rhubarb normally used for 'pulling green' (such as
'Hawke's Champagne') can be forced. It should be assumed that they are
not ready until they have experienced the same number of cold units (160
C°/*300 F°*) as 'Victoria' (see Chapter 28).

The criteria on which one chooses flower cultivars are necessarily more **Flower**
subjective than is the case with vegetables and fruit. The professional cut- **cultivars**
flower grower may be concerned about stem-length, vase-life and other

such market qualities, but these factors apply only to a few species, and are of little concern to the gardener. His interest is in the beauty of the plant as he sees it.

Nevertheless, in the case of plants raised from seed, F1 hybrids are very important where uniformity is required. They are available for the following flowering plants which are raised under glass.

Ageratum	Blue Surf
	Spendthrift
	Blue Danube
Antirrhinum	Humming Bird
	Madame Butterfly
	Little Darling
Begonia (fibrous-rooted)	Pink Avalanche
	Danica Red
Dianthus heddewigii	Queen's Court
	Queen of Hearts
Pelargonium zonale	Red Express
	Playboy
	Susan
Gloxinia	Sutton's Super Perfection
Impatiens sultani (Busy Lizzie)	Grand Prix
	Futura
Tagetes	
African cultivars:	Moonshot
	Yellow Galore
Afro-French cultivars:	Showboat
	Nell Gwyn
Nicotiana	Crimson Rock

Petunia
F1 hybrids have effectively superseded open-pollinated cultivars.

Primula polyanthus	Lemon Punch
	Spring Promise
Primula verna (Primrose)	Colour Magic
Primula obconica	La Scala
Salpiglossis	Splash

The above list merely gives examples of what is available; it is not intended to be exhaustive.

Vegetables and fruits under glass

Chapter 14

Tomatoes

Few plants in the world can have been as intensively studied as the tomato. Its responses to practically every conceivable change in the environment have been carefully logged. So successful have these efforts been that yields under glass of 150 tonnes per hectare (*60 tons per acre*), considered thirty years ago to be excellent, are now regularly doubled. The commercial producer is forced to have high yields of good-quality fruit, but his criteria for quality need not be totally shared by the amateur gardener. The former wants smallish round fruits free from skin blemish and ripening defects. The latter does not mind at all how large his fruits are. The odd *Botrytis* spot on the skin is of no consequence to fruits which do not have to be marketed, and furthermore he is free to grow whatever variety he likes.

Cold house crops

As the majority of garden greenhouses do not have heating systems it is best to consider the cold house crop first. The plants are set out in their growing positions when the temperature of the soil in the greenhouse has reached 14.5°C (*58°F*). This normally takes place in about the third week of April in Britain; a few days earlier in the South and a few later in the North. Planting before this temperature is reached does more harm than good because below it the roots are not active and may even die; the plant stops growing and turns blue. Delaying planting unduly will make the crop both later and smaller.

To prepare for planting, the soil is dug thoroughly and any hard layers below its surface are broken up. It is not recommended to dig in farmyard manure as this can introduce soil pests to say nothing of weed seeds. The best soil conditioner is horticultural peat worked into the surface at the rate of a 9 litre bucketful to each square metre (*2 gall/sq yd*). After this the soil is flooded in the manner already described (see page 31), and when it has drained and the surface has dried the base dressing is applied. This provides the plants with all the magnesium and phosphorus they will need throughout their lives. It is difficult to say precisely what quantities are required but an application of about 70 grams per square metre of keiserite (*2 oz per sq yd*) should supply sufficient magnesium and about 200 grams of superphosphate (*6 oz*) sufficient phosphorus. This dressing is scattered evenly on the surface and raked in. Potassium is also needed to start off the young plants and a dressing of about 70 grams per square metre (*2 oz per sq yd*) of potassium sulphate should suffice.

For best results the young plants should be in 90 mm ($3\frac{1}{2}$ *in*) pots or even better in 110 mm ($4\frac{1}{4}$ *in*) ones, and should have a few flowers, of a bright yellow colour, open on their bottom truss; the plants should be sturdy and squat. They are planted in the soil so that the ball of soil is just below the surface. The soil will already have been flooded so each plant merely needs about $\frac{1}{2}$ litre (*one pint*) of water. Planted at this time of the year they

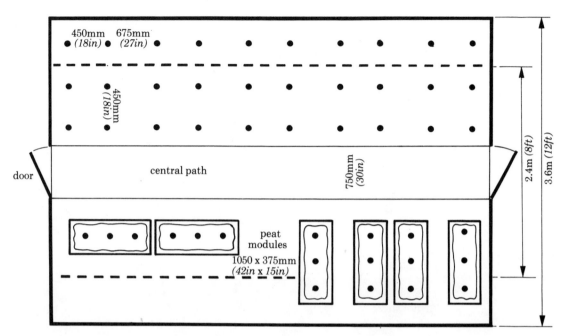

450mm 675mm
(18in) *(27in)*

450mm
(18in)

central path

door

750mm
(30in)

peat
modules
1050 x 375mm
(42in x 15in)

2.4m *(8ft)*

3.6m *(12ft)*

normally get away very quickly and there should be no problems with fruit setting. When planted in the greenhouse soil they are set out in rows along the length of the house. The rows should be from 300 mm *(12 in)* to 350 mm *(14 in)* apart. The distance between the plants within the row is 450 mm *(18 in)* and 680 mm *(27 in)* alternating. This arrangement (see Fig. 32) provides alternative pathways to give better access to the plants. These distances may have come about through long experience: there is considerable disadvantage if they are reduced and little or no gain if they are increased. Each plant needs about a third of a square metre *(0.4 sq yd)* in which to grow and the very early crops only need a quarter of a square metre *(0.3 sq yd)*. If containers are being used instead of the soil the same rules apply.

Fig. 32: tomato planting arrangements in soil (top) or in peat modules (bottom), for two common greenhouse widths. The dashed lines indicate the narrower greenhouse width.

Left: Young tomato plants being trained up vertical strings at a stage of development when deleafing has not yet started.

Right: This tomato plant has been trained around the string in a clockwise direction: it is sometimes argued that the arrangement of tomato leaves on the stem is such that this is more effective than twisting in an anticlockwise direction.

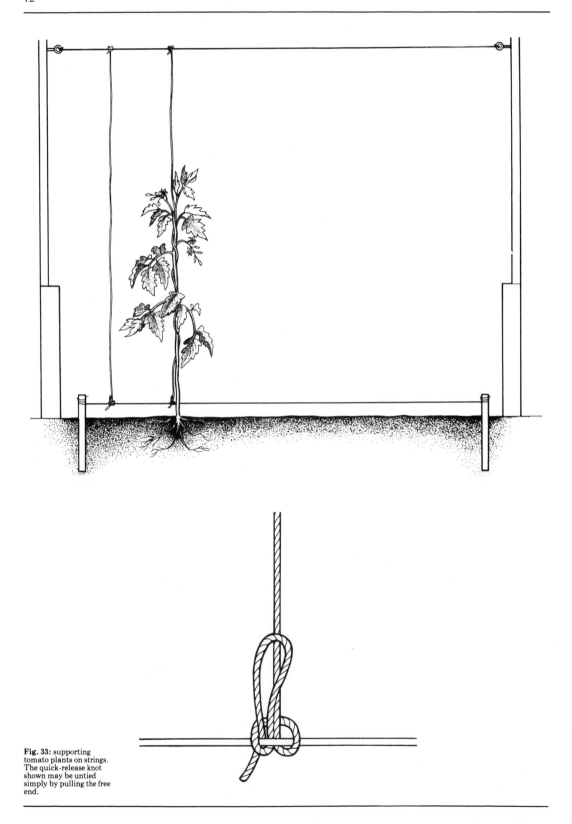

Fig. 33: supporting tomato plants on strings. The quick-release knot shown may be untied simply by pulling the free end.

Tomatoes must be supported from the beginning, and the best method is to twist them round vertical strings. A horizontal wire is run along the soil surface closely parallel to the tomato row and a complementary one is fixed along the roof of the house. The string is then tied top and bottom (see Fig. 33) with enough slack to make it easy to twist it around the tomato stem. Non-rotting artificial-fibre string of immense strength has now replaced the jute string formerly used.

As the plants grow, the side shoots should be removed continually and the growing point of the main stem checked from time to time to see whether it has divided into two, in which case one of the branches must be removed. Cold-house tomatoes rarely have time to ripen six trusses, more usually five, so as soon as the fifth truss has set its fruit there is no point whatever in allowing the stem to continue growing and it should be stopped where there are one or two leaves above it.

Above: A tomato plant being side-shooted — that is to say, the shoot or lateral growing in the axil between leaf and stem is being removed so that the tomato plant grows as a single cordon.
Below: the side shoot removed.

'De-leafing', which is the term used to describe the progressive removal of the lower leaves of the plant, should start when the bottom leaves are shaded by the upper ones and therefore are no longer receiving light. This corresponds roughly with the ripening of the fruit. As each truss swells and individual fruits begin to colour, all the leaves below that truss are best removed. Some growers remove the leaves by bending them upwards so that they snap off cleanly. Most remove them with an upward cut of a sharp knife clean against the stem, leaving no stump or snag: a sure breeding ground for the *Botrytis* fungus which can readily kill the plant.

In sequence: 1. Tomatoes which were planted very early in the year in a heated greenhouse and which have grown to a height of over two metres (6½ft).
2. The first stage in deleafing. The gardener is snapping off the leaves with an upward movement which leaves a clean break on the stem without a snag which could easily become invaded by the ever-present grey mould fungus (*Botrytis cinerea*).
3. Further progress in deleafing.
4. The tomato plants have been deleafed to the correct height in accordance with the development of the truss. Three trusses are exposed and it can be seen that on these the fruits are fully developed and at the point of ripening.

An old-established practice among tomato growers is that of 'damping down' which means spraying the plants all over with a coarse spray of water from a hosepipe. There are two schools of thought about this: the traditional one believes it cools the plant down, increases the humidity around the flower trusses and dislodges the pollen from the anthers to the stigmas, the combined effect being a better fruit set; the opposing view is that the effect is virtually negligible and that to shake the plants vigorously by tapping the supporting strings is sufficient to dislodge the pollen. The probability is that healthy plants properly watered and with the right temperatures will set fruit without any difficulty. There is, however, nothing to be lost by playing safe.

Watering and feeding tomatoes is a subject that was for a long time one of debate and personal judgement. To take watering first: we now know that the tomato probably grows best at a 13 mm ($\frac{1}{2}$ in) deficit. First, the term 'field capacity' must be understood. It means that the soil is holding all the water it can against the force of gravity, all drainage having ceased. Compare it with a bath sponge which when taken out of the water will drip for a time and then will drip no more, but is still wet because if pressure is applied more drips will form. If the sponge were now to be placed in a warm room water would evaporate from it. It is the same with the soil at field capacity; it soon begins to lose moisture into the air both by direct evaporation and by indirect evaporation through the leaves of plants (a process called transpiration).

When the amount of water lost from the soil by evaporation and transpiration equals 13 mm of water or 13 litres/square metre, it can be brought back to field capacity by applying this amount of water (*2.4 gallons per square yard*). The only problem remaining is, how does the amateur tell when his greenhouse soil has a 13 mm deficit? This can be achieved by placing the bottom half of a round tobacco tin or any similar container with vertical sides on top of a pole in the tomato crop so that it is level with the top of the foliage. Then pour water into it to a depth of 13 mm

A battery-powered agitator affectionately called 'the electric bee'. The instrument is placed against a truss of flowers, and when the thumb-switch is pressed the probe vibrates. The agitation of the flower truss causes the pollen to be shed from the anthers onto the stigmas of the flowers. Pollination is very important in tomato plants because flowers which are not pollinated do not develop proper fruits. Tiny fruits on a truss of tomatoes of which the majority are fully developed are often due to bad pollination. Amateurs can achieve a similar result by tapping with a cane the string which supports the tomato, or by agitating the truss with a rabbit's tail tied on the end of a cane.

($\frac{1}{2}$ in) and wait for it to evaporate away. This will coincide with a 13 mm ($\frac{1}{2}$ in) deficit and indicate the need for water which can be applied at any convenient time, day or night. This simple method has been shown to provide a reliable guide to watering and avoids the need for sophisticated equipment.

The next difficulty to be faced is that of applying the water evenly and conveniently. The most satisfactory method is by means of trickle irrigation lines (see Chapter 9). The expense of installation is more than justified by the time saved if the area of the house is large. Feeding the tomato crop during its life is necessary because it is not possible to incorporate into the soil of the greenhouse or into the peat of a module all the nitrogen and potassium it will need. There are two reasons for this: first, it would increase the salinity of the soil to a point where growth was suppressed, and even if this were not the case, the subsequent watering of the crop would cause the nitrogen to be leached out of the soil and upset the nutrient balance.

Liquid feeding has proved to be the most efficient method of dealing with the problem and is one which enables a rapid response to be made to the needs of the crop as displayed by its growth and development.

The alternative method of supplying the crop's needs by top-dressings of fertilisers in powder form is a crude one which allows no precision, although it was one which had to suffice for several decades.

The principle on which liquid feeding is based is that from the moment of planting onwards, every drop of water applied will contain a very small quantity of fertiliser dissolved into it so that by the end of the season the total nutrient need of the crop will have been provided. A crop of tomatoes in a cold greenhouse during its life requires about 38 grams per square metre of nitrogen and 80 grams of potash (K_2O), but only a little over 6 grams of phosphate. Disregarding the phosphate we find we can provide this quantity of nitrogen and potash if during the season we apply, from planting onwards, about 230 litres of liquid feed per square metre (42 gall/sq yd). If we go back to the idea of growing our plants at a 13 mm ($\frac{1}{2}$ in) deficit this means that from the end of April until the middle of September we shall, in fact, be applying our 13 litres of liquid feed per square metre (2.4 gall/sq yd) about 18 times, i.e. about once a week. In dull summers the amount will be less and in bright ones more, but as growth will be relatively less or more the system is self-regulating. The figures are not absolutely precise and are generous.

All we have to work out now is the preparation of the liquid feed and the method of applying it. Of course a number of proprietary brands of liquid feed with instructions for use are available in shops and garden centres, but for the enthusiastic amateur gardener there is no real difficulty in making his own. He needs to purchase two fertilisers (three if he is using peat bags). They are:

    Potassium nitrate (saltpetre)
    Ammonium nitrate
    Mono-ammonium phosphate

All are fertilisers in common horticultural use and the only difficulty likely to be encountered is that of buying them in sufficiently small quantities. This could perhaps be overcome by sharing a large quantity with one or more friends. The ammonium salts must be kept dry in plastic bags tightly tied. The most convenient procedure is to make a concentrated solution of feed which can be stored indefinitely and used as required to make a dilute solution for applying to plants. The concentrated or stock solution is best made in quarts or one-litre batches so that it can be stored conveniently in bottles. The solution consists of:

Potassium nitrate	150 g	*6 oz*
Ammonium nitrate	38 g	*1½ oz*
Water	1 litre	*1 quart*

(Plant nutrient ratio = nitrogen 1 (170 ppm) : potash 2 (335 ppm))

This solution has to be diluted 200 times with water in order to form a liquid feed suitable for application to tomato plants. To keep the rule of watering every time we have a 13 mm deficit ($\frac{1}{2}$ *in*), we have, as stated above, to apply about 13 litres to each square metre, or 2.4 gallons to each square yard. If the water is being applied by means of a watering can, then calculate the number of litres the can holds and put in 5 ml of stock solution for every litre of water – an amount easily measured with a 5 ml medicinal plastic spoon obtainable from any chemist's shop. If working in gallons, a little less than one fluid ounce is required for each one. If a large number of plants is involved then it is worthwhile considering the installation of a trickle irrigation system and a liquid-feeding dilutor. The liquid feed is given immediately after planting and continued until the crop has ceased to grow.

It might be found more convenient to make a larger quantity of liquid feed by having a storage tank with a tap from which watering cans can be filled. Plastic domestic water tanks holding 100–140 litres (*22–30 galls*) give a reasonable reserve, but larger ones fitted with nylon taps are available. Metal tanks, provided they are galvanised, are all right but should have nylon taps to prevent corrosion. If liquid feed, diluted and ready for application, is left in a tank open to the light, green scum, due to the growth of algae, soon appears: so the tank should be covered to exclude light.

Peat bags, or modules as they are more frequently called, offer the best alternative at present once the soil is no longer giving good results. The module is a plastic sack containing peat to which has been added all the trace elements as well as nitrogen, phosphorus, potassium, magnesium and calcium (lime). Several firms produce and sell peat modules and usually issue instructions as to how they should be used. Amateur gardeners are not forced to use proprietory modules, but they will find it infinitely more convenient to do so than to make their own or to use loose peat in troughs.

The peat module bag is made of plastic film and holds about 60 litres (*13 gallons*) or so of peat, enough for three tomato plants to grow satisfactorily. The module is placed on the floor of the greenhouse and slit along its upper surface to within 100 mm or so (*4 in*) from each end and the dry peat is gradually wetted until it has reached container capacity. To prevent the possibility of waterlogged conditions in the base of the module a number of drainage holes are made by stabbing the sides about 20 mm ($\frac{3}{4}$ *in*) above ground level. This should prevent soil-borne diseases gaining access to the peat. The young tomato plants are best if they are raised in peat composts because they then establish more rapidly in the modules than if they had been in loam composts.

While tomatoes in modules need exactly the same amount of water as if they were growing in the soil, the moisture reserve of the compost in the modules is nothing like that of the soil, so watering has to be more frequent. Table 1 gives a very approximate system for calculating the water requirement of tomato plants during the summer months by observing the weather. It shows that on moderately bright days, the amount of water needed is such that if too much moisture stress is not to be put on the plant the modules will really need watering twice, and on very bright days three times. There is really no way round this difficulty other than by the use of trickle irrigation lines, and for those away at work all day there are problems.

Table 1

Weather	Very Dull	Dull	Mod. Bright	Bright	Very Bright
Requirement per plant	$\frac{1}{3}$ litre	$\frac{1}{2}$ litre	1 litre	$1\frac{1}{2}$ litres	2 litres
	$\frac{1}{2}$ pint	$\frac{3}{4}$ pint	$1\frac{3}{4}$ pints	$2\frac{1}{2}$ pints	$3\frac{1}{4}$ pints
per module	1 litre	$1\frac{1}{2}$ litres	3 litres	$4\frac{1}{4}$ litres	6 litres
	$1\frac{3}{4}$ pints	$2\frac{1}{2}$ pints	$5\frac{1}{4}$ pints	8 pints	$10\frac{1}{2}$ pints

Very Dull: Heavily overcast all day
Dull: Generally overcast but occasional breaks in cloud
Mod. Bright: Cloudy with bright intervals
Bright: Mainly sunny with some cloud
Very Bright: Cloudless blue sky all day

Using this system, the time to apply the water is at the end of the day, if only one watering is required, but if two or three then at equal intervals throughout the day. Cold-house crops in modules should be fed in exactly the same way as those growing in the soil, i.e. every watering contains a liquid feed and the feed already stated is the one to use.

The tomato plant gives the best yield if it is grown at a temperature of 18°C (*64°F*) during the day and about 14°C (*58°F*) at night. Unfortunately in an unheated greenhouse the only method of temperature control available is the ventilation system. If the ventilators have automatic controls the thermostat should be set to open the vents at 21°C (*70°F*). If this luxury is not available then you must do your best to open the vents as soon as temperatures shoot up, which they do very quickly in small greenhouses in the summer time. Temperatures over 26°C (*over 80°F*) are more harmful the higher they go and this is when the propping open of doors and taking out of panes of glass mentioned earlier become necessary. It is also necessary to close them when temperatures fall if performance is to be maintained, though actual damage is unlikely from mid-May to mid-September.

Heated greenhouse tomato crops

Techniques of growing tomatoes in heated greenhouses depend on the answers to various questions: How much heating are you prepared to give your plants and for how long are you prepared to give it? When do you hope to pick your first tomatoes? What sort of yield do you expect? By sowing seed in November, installing supplementary lighting, enriching the carbon dioxide content of the air and maintaining the most precise temperatures, you can pick your first tomatoes in April, even earlier in southern England, and carry on until October. Amateur gardeners are rarely prepared to go to such lengths.

Much more likely is the gardener who wants to plant in March in a heated greenhouse in order to get his plants away to a brisk start, keeping the temperature up until the middle of May, and then shutting off until

the cool nights of September when some heat will enable fully formed fruits successfully to ripen. Such an arrangement will permit cucumbers, melons, peppers and aubergines all to be grown in the same house; none to its full potential but good enough for most people's purposes.

The preparation of the soil is exactly the same as for the cold-house crop with the only difference that the quantities of keiserite and potassium sulphate should be slightly increased to about 100 grams each per square metre (*3 oz per square yard*) to allow for the longer growing season and greater activity of the plants.

The liquid-feeding programme will still be the same except that the plants have to be watered in March rather carefully because they might start to grow too rapidly. In that case the bottom truss will not set. If this happens the ammonium nitrate is left out of the feed altogether until they have steadied up. This is more likely to occur in dull springs than in bright ones, but the danger will be over by the middle of April. If later in the season the tops of the plants become thin then the ammonium nitrate in the feed should be increased to 70 grams per litre (*2¾ oz per quart*) to give them more nitrogen and boost their growth.

With peat modules it is advisable for the first two or three weeks after planting to have the peat moist but not at field capacity, which will help to steady up growth until light intensity increases. The watering recommendations given in Table 1 still apply from May onwards, but in March the figures should be reduced to those given in Table 2.

Left: a pot of tomato seeds enclosed within a polythene bag. The bag is placed in an airing cupboard where germination will be rapid. *Right*: the same bag a few days later, after the seedlings have emerged. It will be noted that the seedlings are somewhat drawn and, although they will make quite good plants, it would have been better had they been taken out of the airing cupboard and out of the polythene bag at least twenty-four hours earlier.

Table 2

Weather	Very Dull	Dull	Mod. Bright	Bright	Very Bright
March					
Requirements per plant	125 ml *4 fl oz*	200 ml *6 fl oz*	400 ml *¾ pint*	600 ml *1 pint*	800 ml *1¾ pints*
per module	375 ml *12 fl oz*	600 ml *18 fl oz*	1200 ml *2¼ pints*	2000 ml *3 pints*	2400 ml *5¼ pints*
April					
Requirements per plant	250 ml *7½ fl oz*	375 ml *½ pint*	750 ml *1 pt 6 fl oz*	1125 ml *2 pints*	1500 ml *2¾ pints*
per module	750 ml *1 pt 2½ fl oz*	1125 ml *1½ pints*	2250 ml *4 pints*	3375 ml *6 pints*	4500 ml *8¼ pints*

When the amount of water lost per day is small it need not be replaced until at least 900 ml (*1½ pints*) are needed per module.

The temperatures required to give best results are the same as those for the cold-house crop, the difference being that with a heating system it should be possible to maintain them with reasonable accuracy.

'Ring culture' was a technique which was popular during the 1950s and early 1960s. Young tomatoes are planted into 250 mm (*10 in*) bottomless tubes or collars (rings) made from special paper, roofing felt or even large jam cans in a compost (loam or loamless). The rings are already standing on a bed of gravel or clinker-ash, which in turn is placed over a bed of hardened soil. The plant grows firstly in the compost in the 'ring', but roots soon invade the substrate with some vigour. The theory of management is that feeding roots inhabit the compost and water-imbibing roots ramify in the substrate. Feed is applied copiously in solid fertiliser form to the ring, and water to the substrate. The theory is false but the practice works well enough, although problems with blossom-end rot can be severe. As a technique for avoiding soil-sickness it is burdensome when compared with the peat module, which is superseding it. If it is still done a plastic sheet should separate the substrate from infected soil.

Another technique still practised and worthy of mention is that of grafting tomato cultivars onto root stocks which are tomato species and their hybrids which have resistance to various groups of soil-borne fungal diseases and eelworms. It is a technique which is horticulturally challenging but exacting for the amateur to carry out himself. Sometimes you can buy grafted plants and this may well be worth considering. All in all, peat modules are still hard to beat.

Chapter 15

Cucumbers

The cucumber normally grown in greenhouses (*Cucumis sativus*) is known as the 'English cucumber'. It belongs to the family Cucurbitaceae which includes marrows, melons and gourds. It is exceptional inasmuch as the fruit swells into the familiar cucumber shape without being fertilised. In common with other members of the family both male and female flowers occur on the same plant, and should a female flower by mischance be fertilised then the cucumber swells considerably, forms seeds and develops a bitter flavour. Some call these '*filles mal gardées*'. The first lesson to be learned, then, in cucumber growing is to distinguish between male and female flowers. The male flowers must be removed daily before they have had a chance to shed any pollen onto a passing bee. The female flowers may be identified by the small immature cucumber behind them (see Fig 34).

Cucumber roots are very sensitive to poorly aerated soil and for that reason gardeners soon learned to prepare special beds for growing their cucumber plants, consisting of alternate layers of chopped loam and fresh

Fig. 34: cucumber flowers. The male flower (top right) is easily distinguished from the female with its embryonic cucumber.

Male flowers must be removed daily to prevent the pollination and subsequent fertilisation of the female flowers. This tedious chore can be avoided by growing F1 cultivars which have only female flowers.

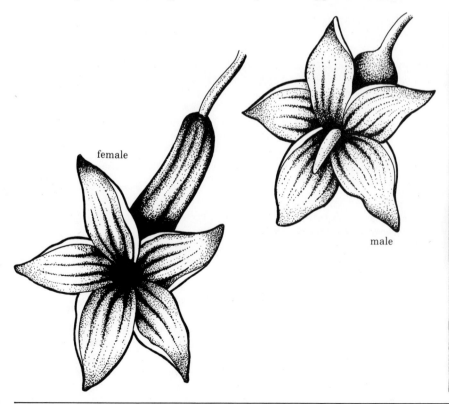

female

male

strawy stable manure. Such methods today would be regarded as too labour-intensive, to say nothing of the difficulty of obtaining fresh strawy manure. The next step in the evolution of growing systems was the use of fermenting straw bales. Later on, when bales became difficult and expensive to obtain, beds were made from consolidated wads of the straw left after combine harvesting. The straw is placed on a sheet of plastic film to isolate it from the soil and is first thoroughly wetted and when it starts to ferment fertilisers are added as follows and gently watered into the straw:

	Straw	100 kg	220 lb
	Ammonium nitrate	600 g	1.3 lb
or	Ammonium sulphate	1 kg	2.2 lb
	Superphosphate	1 kg	2.2 lb
	Potassium nitrate	650 g	1.4 lb
	Ground limestone or chalk	1 kg	2.2 lb

The temperature of the straw starts to rise until it reaches about 50°C (*120°F*) after which it slowly starts to fall. When it has dropped to 38°C (*100°F*) the cucumbers are planted in nests made in the straw in which moist peat has been placed and mounded up sufficiently to accommodate the plant. Once growth gets under way liquid feeding with every watering is essential. In fact, best results are obtained if the peat used on top of the straw for planting is moistened with liquid feed instead of plain water. The recommended feed is made as follows:

Potassium nitrate	150 grams	*24 oz*
Ammonium nitrate	125 grams	*20 oz*
Water	1 litre	*1 gallon*

This is then diluted 200 times, i.e. one 5 ml spoonful in one litre of water (*0.8 fl oz/gallon*). If three or four grams of ground limestone or chalk are mixed in with every litre of peat (*about ½ oz per gallon*) the liquid feed will be more efficacious, and at the same time a further safeguard is to mix in a tiny amount of fritted trace element (Frit 253A).

The liquid feeding programme for the first three weeks after planting is that the beds are watered about every other day with a liquid feed containing only nitrogen. It is made by dissolving 160 grams of ammonium nitrate into one litre of water (*26 oz/gallon*) and diluting this at the usual rate of 5 ml per litre (*0.8 fl oz per gallon*).

Then for the rest of the life of the crop the liquid-feed stock solution is made as follows:

Ammonium nitrate	100 grams	*16 oz*
Potassium nitrate	25 grams	*4 oz*
Magnesium sulphate (Epsom		
Salts)	25 grams	*4 oz*
Water	1 litre	*1 gallon*

The rate of application is as before, 5 ml of the stock solution in one litre of water (*0.8 fl oz per gallon*), applied every other day.

For those who find the straw-bed method too tedious there are, of course, peat modules as described for tomatoes. The liquid-feeding programme is as explained for straw beds, but the addition of lime or frit to the peat in the modules should already have been done by the manufacturer. Some care is needed to ensure that the peat in the modules is not over-watered which would severely damage the sensitive roots of the cucumbers. Three

Young cucumber plants in a peat module. The irrigation line of a trickle-irrigation system can be seen, with one point going to each plant.

plants can be accommodated in each module.

In Holland, Denmark and England (east Yorkshire), large areas of cucumbers are grown on a completely mineral substrate consisting of rockwool, a material developed for the heat-insulation of buildings. It may well be that as experience of its use increases, amateur gardeners will find it provides another method of growing this plant.

Cucumbers require higher temperatures than tomatoes to give best results, and if they are grown in the same house it is inadvisable to try to provide optimum conditions for them, because it will almost certainly be to the detriment of the tomatoes. It is best to provide for the tomatoes and let the cucumbers take their chance. This usually works well enough although the cucumber fruits may be rather large and very early cropping is then out of the question.

From planting out and for their first two months in the greenhouse cucumbers need a night temperature of 19°C (66°F) and a day temperature of 21°C (70°F) with the ventilation being opened when the temperature reaches 27°C (80°F). After this initial period slightly lower temperatures are required, i.e. 17°C (62°F) at night and 19°C (66°F) during the day with ventilators being opened when the temperature reaches 24°C (75°F).

In an unheated greenhouse temperatures such as these cannot be maintained, and it is therefore unwise to plant much before the end of April. If peat modules are being used, which do not provide the heat that comes from straw or manure beds, planting should be delayed until May.

The recommended method of training the plants, because of its

Young cucumber plants in peat modules being grown up strings in a similar manner to tomatoes, as single-cordon plants. It will be noticed that in this arrangement one plant is inclined in one direction and the next in another; this is not essential, but does make a better use of space.

Above right: Cucumbers grown by an extremely modern technique. They are on slabs of rockwool of a kind used for insulating houses; the roots of the cucumber ramify in the rockwool slab, which is wrapped in milky polythene; milky polythene also covers the floor of the greenhouse, the whole providing highly sterile conditions. The rockwool is irrigated frequently with a nutrient solution.

simplicity, is that known as the cordon method. The plant is twisted round a string secured to a wire at bed level and to another at roof level. The string really requires to be about two metres (*6 ft 6 in*) high which means that in most houses it will have to be inclined towards the centre of the house. To prevent an inclined string from sagging it is helpful if it can be secured in some way to the sides of the house at a couple of points along its length. As the plant grows the laterals are removed altogether, save for the last four or five before the plant is stopped, that is when it reaches the top of the string. These are allowed to cascade down, the top of the main stem having been well secured. Male flowers are removed as soon as they appear.

As new roots push out at the base of the stem in the first few weeks they should be covered with a top dressing of the same peat mixture as that in which they were planted originally. If ventilation can be given to prevent temperatures going above the maximum mentioned above, shading on the glass should not be necessary, but otherwise it will be required. Recent investigations have shown that damping down several times a day, which is traditional practice, is not really necessary. Cucumbers are produced in flushes interspersed with periods of low yield.

A special warning must be given to anyone who may be contemplating the straw-bale method of growing. If cereal crops are treated with the herbicides 2, 3, 6–TBA or Picloram the resulting straw may contain residues which could seriously damage the cucumbers (or any other crops). Before buying straw, check that it has not been in contact with these substances.

Chapter 16

Lettuces

After tomatoes and cucumbers, by far the most important food crop grown in greenhouses is the lettuce. Winter and early spring lettuces grown under glass were introduced in the early 1930s and have enjoyed increasing demand ever since. The lettuce is a long-day plant which soon produces flowers ('bolts') when the hours of daylight are long and so lends itself to cultivation under glass in winter. Extensive plant-breeding work has produced lettuces which will grow throughout the winter months when light intensity is low. Plants are produced ready for sale from November onwards. As all the leaves are soft and edible the fact that winter lettuces do not have really very solid hearts does not matter to the consumer. Whether the cost of heating a greenhouse during the winter is worthwhile to the amateur, only he can judge. The temperatures required are by no means high; minimum night temperatures of $4.5°C$ ($42°F$) will suffice provided they are offset by much higher ones when the sun is shining. Better results will come from a higher temperature régime with minimum night temperatures of $12°C$ ($55°F$). Higher temperatures than this produce open-hearted spread-out plants which are undesirable.

Over the years the evolution of the techniques for growing lettuces has been most interesting. Originally the seed was sown in seed trays at four or five hundred to a standard seed tray in JIP 1 compost. The seedlings were then transplanted to other trays at about one and a half inches apart. When the young plants were touching each other they were planted out in the greenhouse about nine or ten inches apart.

Later it was seen that better results came from pricking-off the seedlings from the seed tray straight into their permanent position, thus obviating a second transplanting check to the young plants. The next step was to reduce the number of seeds per seed tray to about two hundred, thus giving each seedling more space and light, and then even better seedlings were found to be obtainable from using JIP 2 compost.

Growers then sought methods of increasing their output of lettuces from the greenhouse – why not two winter crops instead of one? Why not three instead of two? How could this be achieved? The answer turned up in the form of the soil block or lettuce tube. The former was made of compost compressed together by the use of a special machine. The latter was simply a bottomless paper tube filled with compost. The blocks or tubes had the seedling lettuces pricked-out into them and they could be kept close together until they were planted in the greenhouse when half-grown. With careful timing it is obvious that if one full-grown crop is replaced by a half-grown one, output must increase.

This, however, was not the end of the affair. Growers did not really like soil blocks, as they were made of John Innes Compost which posed the difficult problem of obtaining suitable loam. By this time peat as a growing medium had made its début and almost overnight the peat block

This peat module was used last year for growing tomatoes. After the removal of the old crop, the peat was sieved, had a small amount of compound fertiliser mixed into it and was then soaked. It is now growing early lettuces in succession: four lettuces are about one-third grown and another four have just been pricked-off into the peat. In due course more lettuces will be put in, and when the first ones are cut they, in turn, will be replaced with more.

had superseded the soil block. A small 27mm (*1.06 in*) square peat block seems adequate for the purpose and is economical in terms of peat and the space occupied.

The final touch of sophistication was the introduction of pelleted seed. Pelleted seed is a device used by the market gardener to turn small seeds into large ones by embedding them in pills of an inert substance, with the objective of carrying out spaced precision sowing in order to reduce the work of singling and thinning the crop in the field. The advantage of pelleted lettuce seed is that one seed can easily be sown per peat block, thus eliminating all subsequent handling other than that of planting out.

This brief history of winter lettuce production applies to the commercial world. What can the amateur gardener reasonably expect to do in his greenhouse? First, he does not want to produce lettuces in excess of what he can consume and which he has got to sell or give away. He requires only a steady flow of one or two plants per week, from mid-winter onwards. Surely the answer lies in the use of pelleted seed and peat blocks. It is now possible to buy inexpensive 'block makers' and bags of specially prepared block-making peat compost, and to make blocks as required.

In these, lettuce plants can be sown and raised until they are half-grown and then planted into peat modules, one of which will hold ten lettuces, so that two of them should suffice for the whole season. The modules will not want much in the way of water during the winter months, but such as is given should be a liquid feed. There is, of course, no reason why the greenhouse soil should not be used if its fertility has not been affected by soil sickness.

In the future it might come about that pelleted seed is sown in small blocks of rockwool, which are watered with liquid feed; when the seedlings are half-grown the rockwool blocks would stand on a large slab of rockwool where the lettuces could complete their growth.

The first sowing of lettuces should be made in early September (or late August in northern Britain) to produce plants that can be cut from November to Christmas. A sowing in mid- to late-September gives plants which will cut after Christmas, and an October sowing gives plants for February and March. Providing for April and May can be done easily and more cheaply under plastic tunnels or cold frames in the vegetable garden. As will be seen in Chapter 25, lettuce varieties suitable for heated greenhouses are not the same as those suited to over-wintering in cold frames.

One very important point to remember is that lettuces of the butterhead type, such as those grown under glass, will not germinate in high temperatures. The critical point is 25°C (77°F) and the temperature at which they are germinated should be well below this. It is a good idea to spread four or five newspaper pages over the pots or blocks of lettuces. The newspaper is thoroughly soaked and evaporative cooling keeps down the temperature of the compost to safe levels. As soon as germination has taken place, the covering is removed. If pelleted seed is not available, sow three or four seeds to each pot or block and reduce them to one as soon as they have germinated.

Chapter 17

Melons

The melons grown in greenhouses, and if the climate permits in frames, are cultivars of *Cucumis melo*, falling into two distinct groups: musk, netted or English melons, and the French cantaloups. A sub-group within the cantaloups is the Charantais so familiar in France.

As the melon is not a financially viable crop under glass, little work has been done on it and our methods of growing are traditional rather than science-based. The netted or musk melons with their distinctive aroma and flavour are a rare delicacy these days and are probably the kind most worth growing in valuable greenhouse space, although they are more exacting in their requirements, particularly temperature, than the cantaloups.

The melon differs from its relative the cucumber in that its flowers have to be fertilised in order that the fruits can swell; also in that its yield capacity is low, being restricted, for the musk varieties, to a maximum of four fruits and two only if large ones are required. Whatever number of fruits are taken, the female flowers must all be fertilised on the same day or as near as possible to it. Otherwise those fertilised later fail to develop equally with those fertilised earlier, and may even shrivel and abort. This problem is not so acute with the stronger-flavoured cantaloups which can carry as many as six fruits of reasonable size in warm summers.

Melons supported by a wigwam of canes. This method is not easy to arrange if the melons are being grown in peat modules.

Another related problem is that the female flowers occur mostly on sub-laterals, of which enough must be available to provide the requisite number of flowers for pollination at the same time. The method of training them must therefore produce the necessary number of sub-laterals. Methods vary: one way is to stop the plant when about 150 mm (*6 in*) high and allow two laterals to be produced. These then produce sub-laterals which are tied to horizontal wires running the length of the house. Another is to allow the plant to grow taller before it is stopped so that four laterals can be produced. These laterals are again tied to horizontal wires and may be stopped to encourage the production of sub-laterals. These traditional methods necessitate the installation of a trellis of wires along the roof of the house which it is tedious to provide and very difficult to arrange in metal houses. Another possibility is to twist the melon around a string in the fashion of a cordon cucumber until it is stopped at about 450 mm (*18 in*). Then of the resulting laterals one is trained up the original string and three of the remainder are selected to grow up three neighbouring strings. Unwanted laterals are removed and each plant then occupies four strings.

Whichever method of training is adopted, the plants are kept under surveillance until some seven or more fully-developed female flowers are open. As with cucumbers, female flowers are easily recognised by the small undeveloped melon behind them. This is totally absent from male flowers. Pollination is best achieved by picking male flowers, pulling back the petals and pushing the stamens (which should be shedding pollen) into the

sub-
laterals

s

female flower so that its stigma is surrounded by the cluster of stamens. If sufficient male flowers are available, which should be the case, place one in each female flower. If pollination is successful fertilisation will follow and the fruits will start to swell. They should be reduced in number to a

Some melons supported on a wigwam of canes. The fruits are near to ripening and are being supported in melon nets. By this time water is being withheld, and the lower leaves are beginning to wilt.

maximum of four for the musks and six for the cantaloups. When they are about the size of cricket balls they have to be supported in specially made melon nets. If these cannot be obtained then some sort of sling must be made to support them, or the vine will be dragged down. Nets can be made from old strawberry netting.

Melons have, in the past, been grown in specially constructed beds made of chopped loam and well-rotted manure in the proportions of about seven parts loam to one of manure. For early crops these beds were built on staging over a heating pipe, or, at an earlier period still, over a manure hot-bed. Enthusiasts today could achieve this by building a bed or placing peat modules over electrical soil-warming cables, but for main crops it is difficult to see how the peat module, without bottom heat, can be improved upon. A normal peat module will, as with cucumbers, accommodate three plants grown on the cordon system, or two if they are trained against horizontal wires.

Melons are very susceptible to a rotting of the neck of the plant, known as collar rot. To guard against this, traditional practice has been to plant the young plants to only half the depth of the ball of compost in which they are growing. As they root, the compost above the planting level gradually washes off leaving the tops of the roots exposed so that they harden and resist infection. Another method, in the days of clay pots, was to knock the bottom out of the pot in which the young melon had been grown and plant this to half its depth, thereafter taking care never to water inside its rim. If peat modules are used the danger of collar rot should be eradicated.

In a steady temperature of 27°C (80°F) melons grow rapidly and two or even three crops can be produced in a year; however the melons would still prove very expensive. To be more realistic, 21°C (70°F) is considered to be a suitable temperature – similar to that suitable for cucumbers. The minimum night temperature should be 18°C (65°F) and during the day the ventilators should be opened when it reaches 27°C (80°F). If they are to be grown along with cucumbers, tomatoes and other plants they will take longer to develop and the number of fruits may have to be reduced. In this case it may prove much safer to grow cantaloup varieties which are tolerant of lower temperatures and with which success is more certain. In good summers in the south of England cantaloups can be grown successfully in unheated houses, but in the north results can be disappointing and it is essential to raise young plants with some heat.

Liquid feeding programmes have not been developed for melons but it is normal to start feeding once the fruits have reached the cricket-ball size. The liquid feed recommended for cucumbers should be used. The peat in the modules is kept well watered until ripening commences. At the onset of ripening a network of so-called veins appears on the fruits. Watering from then on virtually ceases and more ventilation is given. By the time they are ripe the leaves will be flagging, and there will be a strong aroma of melon. The time to cut is indicated by cracks developing around the base of the stalk. When cutting it is usual to sever the lateral from which the fruit is hanging and to leave a piece of it on either side of the stalk, thus providing a convenient handle.

Chapter 18

Other vegetables and herbs

The sweet (or green) pepper, *Capsicum annuum*, and the aubergine or egg plant, *Solanum melongena*, are two plants requiring similar cultivation which have become increasingly popular in recent years.

Peppers and aubergines

Peppers come in all shapes and sizes, with small-fruited dwarf varieties being used as decorative pot plants and the more vigorous larger-fruited kinds for salad and culinary purposes. Both peppers and aubergines are close relatives of the tomato and respond to similar conditions. The temperature, water and nutritional needs of the plants are identical with those of the tomato. They can be grown in the greenhouse soil or in pots, but most easily in peat modules. In heated greenhouses they can be planted from mid-February until mid-April according to how early and large a yield is required. Most people will be satisfied with a mid- to late-March planting along with their tomato plants. The cold house crop is sown in mid-March and planted in mid-May.

It is usual to plant at a density of three plants per square metre. As the amateur is likely only to want a few plants it might be more convenient to think in terms of plants being set out 390 mm ($15\frac{1}{2}$ in) apart in the row with 460 mm (*18 in*) between the rows if more than one row is required.

The method of training peppers depends upon the numbers being grown. Where this is large 200 mm (*8 in*) mesh wire, string or plastic netting is often used, being supported horizontally above the plants. The amateur will find it easier to provide a single string as for tomatoes. The leading shoot is twisted round the string and the four or five side shoots which are allowed to remain are tied loosely round at intervals. Though it is not essential, the first flower is usually removed to encourage the development of lateral shoots.

For aubergines a single string can be used, or if they are in pots they can be tied to a cane.

Both the dwarf and the climbing forms of the French bean (*Phaseolus vulgaris*) are tropical plants from South America and can be grown in greenhouses in order to have fresh pods early in the season. Deep-freeze enthusiasts will probably have no interest in growing French beans under glass because they will grow sufficient of both French and runner beans out of doors to provide a whole year's supply.

French beans

Early supplies of dwarf French beans can be obtained by sowing about six seeds in peat compost in a 250 mm (*10 in*) 'whalehide' pot. The compost is thoroughly soaked and after it has drained back to container capacity the seeds are pressed into the compost about 25 mm (*1 in*) deep. After germination the number is reduced to four. A temperature of 18°C (*65°F*) is needed for full success so the plant cannot be considered worthwhile in its own right but only as a catch-crop, i.e. one grown in the space that will later be required by the main crop. Dwarf French beans in this rôle match

Four climbing French beans, which have been pre-germinated, have been put into a used peat module; they will ultimately climb up the strings and provide French beans long before the outdoor crop is ready.

in well with cucumbers. The pots are placed alongside the cucumbers and should have produced their pods and have been harvested by the time the former are overshadowing them completely.

A much more worthwhile proposition is the climbing French bean, which produces a larger yield over a longer period. The method of growing this form of the plant is to sow the seeds singly in 64 mm ($2\frac{1}{2}$ in) biodegradable containers, or in small peat blocks, and then to plant them when two rough leaves have formed, into either the greenhouse soil or peat modules. They are then grown up strings fixed in the same way as for tomatoes. About six plants can be accommodated in a peat module. They can be grown in cold houses from plantings made in late April to give yields about a month or six weeks before outside crops.

The scarlet runner bean (*Phaseolus multiflorus*) is not grown under glass because without hand pollination it will not set fruits, and it is not considered to be worth the trouble or space required.

Mint

Before the days of deep-freezing and processing, early supplies of mint were grown under glass. Enthusiasts for the fresh product may still do this, but to avoid losing their plants by devastating attacks of fungus causing the disease of mint rust, should obtain the variety known as apple mint. The roots are dug up from the garden in November or December after some cold weather has been experienced. They are washed clean, dried and then planted in the greenhouse soil. The method of planting is to excavate a trench 75 mm (*3 in*) deep, about 300 mm (*12 in*) wide and no more than a metre (*3 ft 3 in*) in length. The soil should previously have been flooded and drained back to field capacity. The roots are laid quite thickly in this trench and then covered over and watered. In due course the mint will appear, very early if the house is heated and later but well before the outdoor crop if it is not.

Mustard and cress

The production of this salad crop has now become highly specialised and is done on a very large scale by a few producers who send their supplies all over the country. However, only the cress is produced, so those who want the tang of mustard in the mixture must grow their own. The method is to sow the cress on the surface of a layer of peat in a plastic seed tray, and the mustard in the same way in a different tray two days later. In both cases the seed is not covered with compost but with polythene. If the temperature can be kept at 15°C (*60°F*) the seedlings should be about 50 mm (*2 in*) high within six or seven days. They are then ready for cutting and the two can be mixed in whatever proportion is preferred. The flimsy plastic containers in which cress is now bought can be washed and used for home production.

Early potatoes

This is a very worthwhile catch-crop for the British amateur who wants the pleasure of having his own early potatoes fresh from the soil in late April or May in preference to those imported from the Mediterranean countries. While it is best to use certified 'sets' or 'seed' they are often not available in time to make the early start that is required and so it is necessary to select sets from the previous home-grown garden crop. Ideally the potatoes selected should be no more than 60 grams (*2 oz*) in weight and must come from healthy plants.

Early potatoes if left until they are mature become very large and much less suitable for the purpose, so they should be selected from early potato varieties that are being lifted when they are about this size. When lifted they are washed clean and dried and placed in a box with a slatted bottom so that the 'rose' ends are uppermost. The 'rose' end of a potato is that where most of the eyes are concentrated. The tray is kept in a frost-proof shed until mid-December. At this time the tray should be placed in a frost-proof greenhouse to encourage 'chitting' – the term used to describe the potato tuber's production of shoots.

In mid-January the sets are placed singly in 225 mm (*9 in*) pots. The so-called 'whalehide' paper pot is suitable. The pot is half-filled with compost, either John Innes or loamless, the set is placed in position and the pot is then filled to the top loosely and watered. This will bring about the necessary degree of consolidation. If compost is thought to be too expensive garden soil mixed with peat in the proportion of 2 to 1 can be used, but this involves the risk of disease. A temperature of 7°C (*45°F*) is all that is required and it can drop lower than this provided the shoots have not emerged. Once they have, frost protection is essential. In cold houses a later start will be necessary and perhaps some extra protection in severe weather. Once the shoots are about 150 mm (*6 in*) high it is wise to start liquid feeding with every watering, using the feed recommended for pot plants. Do not be tempted to look for potatoes before the end of April, because before then the plant will not have received enough light for tuber production.

Potato tubers being chitted (or sprouted) in a greenhouse, so that when planted out in the garden they will give earlier and heavier yields. Note that the potatoes have been packed in a tray so that their 'rose' ends are uppermost; these are the ends where the sprouts grow.

Chapter 19

Strawberries and grapes

Strawberries

Forced strawberries are a challenging crop for the amateur to grow. Being able to produce fruit in March and April, before outdoor crops are ready, makes for a great deal of satisfaction. The most popular cultivar for the purpose used to be 'Royal Sovereign' because of its natural earliness, superb flavour and light foliage. Healthy stocks are now difficult to come by and one of the modern cultivars such as 'Cambridge Vigour' will almost certainly have to be used instead.

The technique is to root runners as early as possible from outdoor strawberries during their first season when they are young and vigorous. Rigid plastic pots 75 mm (*3 in*) in diameter are filled with a loamless peat compost and plunged into the soil between the strawberry rows level with its surface. Runners are then secured with a wire hoop so that rooting can take place into the pot. Runners form in June and should be well rooted by July. Before the end of the month the pots are lifted and detached from the parent plant. Each pot should be examined carefully to ensure that there are no earthworms. To do this, gently tap the plant out of the pot to examine the root ball for evidence. The pots should be stored close together in the open on a layer of peat or sand over a polythene sheet where they are kept well watered.

In early September they are transferred to 150 mm (*6 in*) diameter pots and placed back 'pot thick' on the standing area where they remain at least until January. It is desirable for the standing-down bed to be in a cold frame so that, when necessary, the pots can be protected against adverse weather. Frost or snow may crack the pots and wind may cover them with debris.

Strawberry runners being pegged down into a pot to give an early-established plant for growing under glass later. Strawberries rooted in this fashion may have the pots invaded by earthworms, and a careful check for these should be made before they are placed on a standing-down bed prior to going into the greenhouse.

Strawberries in pots in a greenhouse with the flowers well-formed. The photograph was taken early in May.

There was a belief among older gardeners that the pots of strawberries had to be placed near the glass and so it was traditional to erect shelves specifically for this purpose. There is no real merit in doing this, but it is important to remember that the plants require the maximum amount of light available. They are brought into the greenhouse in January, whether or not it is heated, and placed on the staging close together until growth commences. Then they are gradually 'roomed-out' as necessary. Once growth is under way, liquid feeding as recommended for pot plants should be given with each watering.

Strawberries do not require high temperatures: until growth starts the minimum night temperature should be 7°C (45°F); once growth is under way it should not fall below 10°C (50°F) and during the flowering and fruiting period a minimum of 13°C (55°F) is desirable.

A traditional pollination method: a rabbit's tail on a cane being used to pollinate a cherry flower.

The flowers open at a time when no pollinating insects are on the wing and so it is necessary to pollinate the flowers by hand. The gardener's traditional method is to dust the flowers with a rabbit's tail, affixed to the end of a cane. A sable paint brush or cotton wool are equally good. Pollination needs to be done daily and the middle of the day is said to be the best time, though it is difficult to see why this should be. As soon as the fruits begin to swell and the truss begins to droop, it needs to be supported by means of a forked stick or wire cradle to prevent the fruits resting on the compost in the pot and being splashed when it is watered. To ensure large, even fruits the trusses are usually thinned to six fruits only.

When growing under glass strawberries are very susceptible to attack by powdery mildew. This can be controlled and prevented by the use of the fungicide Benomyl (sold under the trade name 'Benlate'), which should be watered onto the pots as soon as they are brought into the greenhouse. It should also be sprayed on the plants when they are growing, and again when the fruit is set. This treatment should also prevent rotting of the berries caused by the grey mould fungus *Botrytis*.

Grapes

Producing grapes under glass played such an important part in the history of greenhouses that the standard house, 10 m (30 ft) wide, became known as a vinery. In the island of Guernsey, greenhouses are still called vineries by everyone. The growing of grapes was not only a major preoccupation of the private gardener, but was a substantial business on the part of the commercial grower as well. With the introduction of refrigerated cold storage on ships early this century the commercial industry dwindled away, as, more gradually, did the private garden supply, for different reasons.

For the amateur, vine growing is not possible in small greenhouses but once the width of the greenhouse reaches about five metres (*15 ft*) the possibility exists.

Grapes are grown normally on a single cordon system, i.e. a single stem, or rod as it is called, is produced over a period of about four years. This rod produces laterals each year on which the bunches of grapes are borne, and at the end of the season these laterals are pruned back to basal buds so that in the winter all that remains is the rod. As the years go by, the points from which the laterals arise gradually become gnarled spurs.

Vines are propagated from dormant shoots known to gardeners as hardwood or leafless cuttings. A lateral shoot of ripened wood is obtained in January or February and is divided by cutting it about 25 mm (*1 in*) each side of a strong bud to form a 'vine eye'. This is placed in a 75 mm (*3 in*) pot horizontally so that the bud is just peeping through the compost, and the pot is then placed in a propagating case (or propagator) where it can be kept moist and at a temperature of about 15°C (*60°F*) until the bud has grown and roots have formed in the pot. The pot is then removed from the greenhouse staging until it is full of roots, at which point the young vine is re-potted into a 150 mm (*6 in*) pot. While still in the small pot the standard pot-plant liquid feed is used to prevent a check through starvation. The same applies after re-potting because vigorous growth is required. The young rod must be tied to a cane to ensure an erect stem. A heated greenhouse is not required after the propagation stage, and when autumn comes the young plant needs to ripen its wood in the coolest conditions possibly obtainable under glass, and by allowing the compost to become much drier than when growth was active.

The following season for the young vine starts in February or March according to whether it is in the south or north of England. The first operation is the drastic one of cutting the stem back to within one or two buds of the base. The pot is then well watered and, ideally, placed in a house with a minimum night temperature of 13°C (*55°F*), which will cause growth to start. Liquid feeding must continue from the beginning. In May the plant should be transferred to a 250 mm (*10 in*) pot. As an alternative

Young vines which have been propagated from eyes. One plant has been removed from the soil to show the extensive root system.

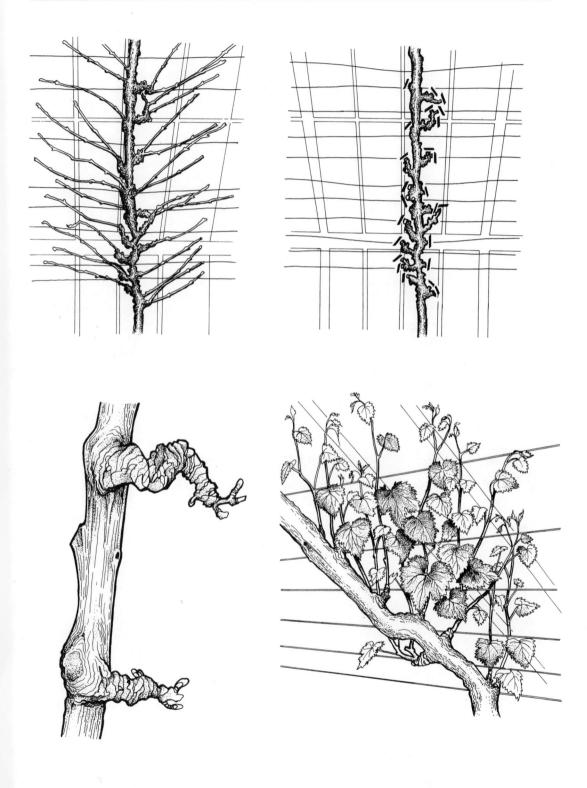

to the exacting liquid-feeding régime slow-release fertilisers can be mixed into the compost, and if this method is chosen the transfer to the large pot becomes essential. This second season of growth is very much the same as the first: after April heat in the house is no longer required; excessive temperatures are avoided by adequate ventilation; the pot is watered so that it never becomes in the least dry until the wood starts to ripen in the autumn; lastly the young rod as it grows is tied to a two-metre (6 ft) cane and any side shoots which form are removed. The rod is now ready for planting in its permanent position.

Private gardeners used to go to most elaborate lengths to prepare the site where vines were to be planted, excavating the soil to the depth of three spades and replacing the subsoil with chopped meadow loam. Sometimes the roots were enclosed within a chamber made by excavating a pit one metre (3 ft) deep, concreting the base and building brick walls on it up to the soil surface. Bricks at the base of the walls were omitted at intervals to provide drainage. The chamber was then filled with chopped loam to which lime, bonemeal and manure had been added. In modern greenhouses the vine roots will almost certainly escape into the soil outside; but this does not matter unduly. All that is really required is normal digging, unless there is a hard layer of 'pan' below the surface, in which case it should be broken by double digging, i.e. digging to a depth of two spades. If well rotted farmyard manure is available it can be dug into the soil in generous amounts, and thoroughly mixed in, but an equally generous application of horticultural peat would probably be a wiser course of action. When digging is complete the planting area should be dressed with a compound fertiliser having an analysis of 12 per cent nitrogen, 12 per cent soluble phosphate and 18 per cent potash (K_2O) or thereabouts. This is scattered evenly over the soil surface at a rate of 120 grams per square metre (4 oz per sq yd), and raked in lightly, after which the site is flooded in the manner already described.

The rod is planted in the greenhouse at any time in the autumn about 300 mm (1 ft) from the outside wall of the greenhouse and cut back to a bud leaving about one metre (3 ft) of rod. If more than one vine is planted they should be separated by about one metre (3 ft). Vines are supported on a trellis of wires which run along the length of the house some 225 mm (9 in) from the glass and 300 mm (1 ft) apart. The rod is trained so that it follows the form of the house; in a full-sized vinery it is stopped at the ridge, but in the smaller houses with which the amateur is more likely to be concerned it may continue down the other side of the house as far as the bottom wall. The lateral growths are, of course, tied to the horizontal wires. Another method of support, which may suit the amateur better, is to affix a wire to the wall of the house and take it up to the ridge and down again to the opposite wall. At the ridge it is supported by a wire sling 225 mm (9 in) long so that it can be put under tension. Other wire slings support it at intervals along its length. The wires are positioned at 450 mm (18 in) intervals so that the rod can be tied to one and the laterals to those on either side. This method avoids having wires in that part of the house where vines are not being grown. Both systems are easy to install in a timber house, but it is much more difficult in a metal one where some sort of support system, independent of the house, to which the wires can be affixed may be necessary. Number 10 gauge wire should be used.

During its first season after planting, the vine is allowed to extend its rod as far as it will go. Laterals which grow from the older part of the rod are

A grapevine growing as a single cordon against a support system provided within the greenhouse. The spurs on either side of the cordon, from which the shoots are annually produced, can be clearly seen.

tied in and stopped when 450 mm (*18 in*) long and any sub-laterals which appear are stopped at one leaf. The soil should be brought back to field capacity when a 13 mm ($\frac{1}{2}$ *in*) deficit has formed (the method of assessing moisture deficit recommended for tomatoes – see page 75 – can be used equally well for vines). A trickle irrigation system capable of wetting the area of soil occupied by the vine is very helpful. In August the wood starts to ripen and watering is reduced to aid the process by allowing a 50 mm (*2 in*) deficit to build up. Heat is only required at the beginning of the season. When the leaves have fallen the laterals are pruned back to one bud, and the rod is reduced so that its total length is about $2\frac{1}{2}$ m (*8 ft*). This pruning must always be done immediately after leaf fall when bleeding will not occur. The second season after planting should be an exact repeat of the first year, except that at pruning time the rod may well be long enough to prune back to its allotted length, which will be either to the ridge of the house or to the bottom of the glass on the other side. As you will by now be getting impatient you can allow two bunches of grapes, one on each of the lower laterals.

The third year after planting may be regarded as a fruiting year and one in which the routine management programme is followed. The first operation is the application of the fertiliser of the kind and at the rate given previously. The 'border' as it is called is then flooded, the ventilation closed and the heat put on to start the plant into growth. The precise time when this is done depends on what can be afforded. A cultivar such as 'Black Hamboro' can be started in January to produce grapes in June, but can be started later. A mid-season cultivar such as 'Muscat of Alexandria' would not be started before mid-February and would yield in September; while a later one such as 'Gros Colmar' would be started in March with a minimum of heat and would not yield until October with perhaps some heat needed to keep frost out of the house. The starting temperature for vines is 7°C (*45°F*). As growth develops and light intensity increases the minimum night temperature is gradually raised to 15°C (*60°F*) when the vines are in flower. The 'Muscat' varieties set their flowers better if higher temperatures can be given, which is probably a deterrent to growing them. Daytime temperatures should not be allowed to rise above 24°C (*75°F*). The atmosphere of the house should be moist and this is achieved by keeping the soil surface wetted to provide the water for evaporation.

The number of laterals has to be regulated by rubbing out the surplus when they are very short. In young vines an excess is unlikely but in older ones considerable reduction is necessary. About 150 mm (*6 in*) is the smallest distance that can be allowed between them. They are tied to the wires and stopped at the second leaf beyond the flowers. This causes sub-laterals to form and these are stopped at one leaf.

When the flowers are open the rods are tapped to shake the pollen from the anthers onto the stigmas. Dusting with a rabbit's tail (or equivalent) is another aid to pollination frequently used, as is the maintenance of high relative humidity during the flowering period. Once fertilisation is achieved and indicated by the swelling of the berries, day temperatures are reduced by increased ventilation.

The next operation is that of thinning, a chore essential for success, but loathed by gardeners because of its tedium. Thinning is traditionally done with grape scissors and a forked stick, care being taken not to touch the berries and remove the bloom from them. About 65–75 per cent of all the berries that form in a bunch must be removed. Although Victorian gardeners would turn in their graves at the thought, grapes can be thinned with finger and thumb provided it is done at a very early stage of development and before any bloom has formed. The number of bunches also has to be reduced to allow about one bunch per 300 mm (*1 ft*) of rod.

Traditional watering practice was to flood the border before the vine had started to grow, again just before the flowers opened, and then again after thinning. Unfortunately careful perusal of the older literature gives no indication of how much water constituted a flooding. Today we would not use such terms; we prefer more precise ones such as field capacity and moisture deficit. Vines should be grown at a 13 mm ($\frac{1}{2}$ *in*) deficit until the berries are fully developed and beginning to colour. The soil can then be allowed to become much drier, developing as much as a 45 mm (*1.8 in*) deficit, which will aid ripening of fruit and wood. Such a watering régime will avoid the splitting of berries.

The development of the berries is not an even process but a phased one. After fertilisation they swell rapidly until they are about the size of small garden peas, the size at which they are normally thinned. They then stop swelling for at least ten days during which time the pips harden. Then they start to swell again until they have reached their final size after which they begin to colour. Ripening is a slow process during which the berries are vulnerable to sun scald and 'shanking'. The former is caused by overnight condensation on them followed by strong sunshine. It can be avoided by ventilating early enough in the morning to ensure that the moisture evaporates before the sunshine is too strong. 'Shanking' is a condition which causes the stalks of the berries to shrivel followed by the withering of the berries themselves. The exact cause of shanking is unknown but it has long been regarded as a natural aborting of the fruit when the rod is carrying more than it can support. Stopping laterals which have been allowed to grow too long, subsoil dryness, or impeded drainage, are also considered to be possible contributory causes.

The liquid feeding of grapes has not been the subject of detailed study as with tomatoes and cucumbers, but there are good grounds for believing that the standard tomato feed with a ratio of nitrogen to potash of 1 : 2 given at every watering would more than adequately replace all the mulching with farmyard manure and applications of dried blood recommended in older books. This would leave only phosphate to be applied as a solid fertiliser at 30 g/sq m (*1 oz per sq yd*) every spring for the first three or four years and then repeated every third year or so thereafter.

The season ends with the cutting of the bunches, pruning back laterals after leaf fall, and stripping away loose bark from the rod.

A lean-to vinery house in which old-established grapevines are growing as single cordons against a specially-prepared support system of trellis wires to support the annual shoots and iron stanchions to support the vine rods.

Chapter 20

Peaches and nectarines; figs

The cultivation of peaches under glass has been practised as long as that of the vine. They are best grown as fan trees, a form well suited to the fruiting habit of the species. Fan-trained trees are now difficult to purchase and very expensive because of the skilled craftsmanship required for their production. This provides the amateur gardener with a challenge to produce his own.

Peaches are budded by nurserymen onto two kinds of rootstocks known as common Mussell and Brompton. However, these may be difficult to obtain, so instead a seedling peach obtained by raising rootstocks from peach stones can be used. The rootstocks are planted 300 mm (*1 ft*) apart in a row and are budded in June. The buds must be obtained from an existing peach or nectarine, preferably one of the well-known early cultivars such as 'Duke of York', 'Hale's Early' or 'Peregrine' from among the peaches, or 'Cardinal' or 'Early Rivers' from among the nectarines. Space does not permit a description of the technique of budding but the new method known as chip-budding is perhaps the easiest to practise. The following February the rootstock is cut back to a point just above where the bud was inserted, and the subsequent summer's growth should result in the production of a strong shoot which should be tied to a cane.

When winter comes the young shoot is cut back to a height of 450 mm (*18 in*), the cut being made just above a bud. The following summer (the third) the shoots which arise from the buds below this cut are tied to canes so that they are almost at right angles to the main stem, half on one side of it and half on the other. This training must be done in the summer while the

Peaches and nectarines

Below left: a peach tree trained as a fan against a supporting trellis affixed to a wall. The original training of the fan has not been done with sufficient expertise to produce a fan in which all the ribs were of roughly the same size, but nevertheless it covers the area provided for it quite satisfactorily.
Below: a young fan-trained peach tree where the technique of producing an evenly-balanced fan was not understood at all: through ignorance and neglect, one particular branch has become so dominant that all the remaining ribs of the fan are suppressed.

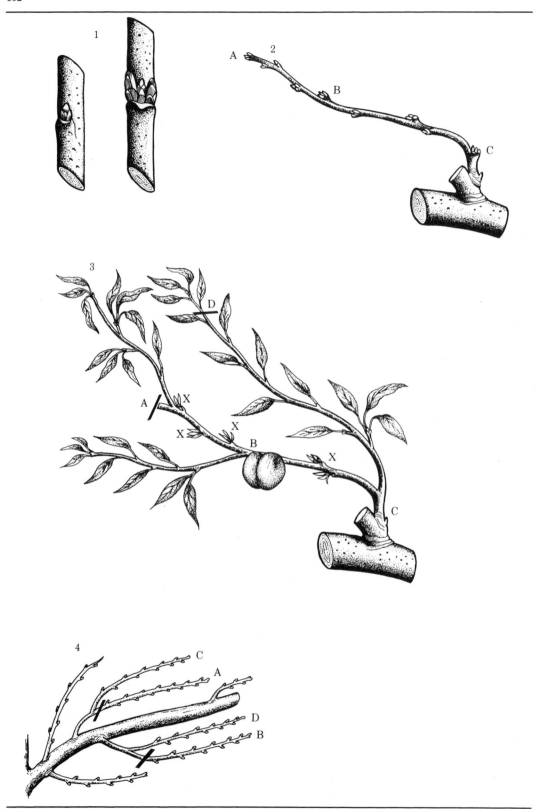

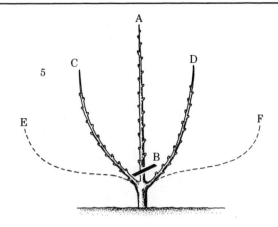

5

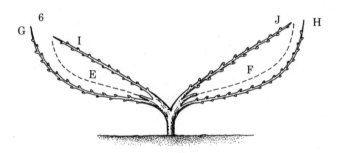

6

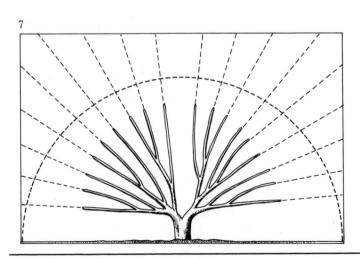

7

Fig. 37: the renewal system of pruning peaches. **1:** Sections of a one-year-old ripened peach shoot showing a leaf-bud (left) and a leaf-bud between two flower-buds (right). **2:** A ripened one-year-old shoot which has been cut back to A. Most of the buds will develop both flowers and leafy shoots, but only the leafy shoots at A, B, and C will be allowed to develop, all others being removed. In the autumn everything will be cut back, leaving only the renewal shoot which has grown from C. **3:** The summer growth from the shoot depicted in (2). Only one blossom has been allowed to form a fruit, and at X leafy shoots have been removed at an early stage. Autumn pruning cuts will be at C and D to leave a ripened shoot similar to that shown in (2). **4:** A branch of a fan-trained peach showing how the two-year-old shoots A and B, which have fruited, are removed and replaced by the younger shoots C and D. **5:** The single stem A of a one-year-old maiden tree is cut at B in the autumn. C and D are the resultant growths, which are tied down to E and F on the support system. **6:** In the winter (year 2) E and F are cut back as shown. G, H, I and J are the resulting shoots as tied down to the support wires: I and J are tied in as they grow to prevent them dominating and suppressing G and H. **7:** Pruning back the four shoots in (6) in the autumn of year 3 produces four shoots on each side, and further cutting back in year 4 causes the tree to acquire its final complement of about nine branches on each side of the fan.

shoots are young and pliable. In winter the young shoots are pruned back to two or three buds which should produce in the following summer, the fourth since budding, a sufficient number of branches to form a fan with 12–18 ribs. The shoots which form these branches must be carefully tied to canes so that when the wood ripens in the autumn they have become branches in the desired positions. (See Fig. 37.)

Fan-trained peaches can be grown most conveniently against south-facing walls in lean-to houses. One tree requires about 4 m (*13 ft*) of length of wall and 4 m (*13 ft*) in height. In free-standing houses they are planted 300 mm (*1 ft*) away from the greenhouse wall and grown on wire trellis fixed the same distance from the glass. A third method is to plant the tree in the centre of the house and have the fan crosswise. This requires a house not less than 6 m (*20 ft*) wide. Whatever method is used, growing peaches cannot be contemplated unless the space is available.

The preparation of the soil is the same as is recommended for vines. The young tree is planted in November, and in the first season heat is not required. In January the branches are tied to the trellis so that they are in as near a regular fan shape as possible, with the bottom ribs being slightly below the horizontal and pruned back to half their length. Throughout the summer the young tree should be grown at a deficit of about 40 mm ($1\frac{1}{2}$ *in*), but the surface of the soil should be damped daily to prevent the air in the house becoming dry. No precise information on the watering and nutritional needs of peaches is available, but it would be reasonable to assume that if the phosphate and lime needs of the soil are provided for in its initial preparation, then liquid feeding at the standard dilution rate of 1 in 200 with the tomato feed (nitrogen : potash = 1 : 2) should be correct. For vines and soil-grown crops generally the pot-plant feeds contain too much nitrate and will cause the soluble-salt concentration to become too high. In any event, during the winter the soil must be flooded as a safeguard against any build-up of nitrates which may have occurred during the summer.

The first year in the greenhouse is a training year, and any blossoms that form are removed. As shoots sprout from the ribs they have to be thinned when about 50 mm (*2 in*) long as follows: all breast-wood shoots (i.e. those not growing sideways but out from the fan) are removed, and other shoots are tied to the trellis so that they are no closer than 75 mm (*3 in*) apart and ideally at an angle of 30° above the horizontal. These shoots will bear fruit the following season. Those for which there is no room are removed. The main ribs or branches are allowed to extend, then at the end of the season they are shortened back by about a third; this process is repeated annually until they have reached the end of the space allotted to them. Throughout the first year the ventilators should be kept fully open day and night. In the autumn the fallen leaves are removed, and the trees are sprayed with a winter wash to kill the eggs of over-wintering pests.

The second season will be the first fruiting one in which the regular pruning is practised. This method is known to fruit growers as a 'renewal system' (see Fig. 37). It is accomplished as follows: the shoot that was tied in during the previous summer will have buds along its length and at its end; many of these will break into growth; when these growths are about 50 mm (*2 in*) long all but three, one at the base, one in the middle and one at the end, should be removed; after leaf-fall everything is cut back to the bottom shoot, which is then tied-in to replace the one from the base of which it grew, thus renewing or replacing it. As the main ribs of the fan

extend each year, the number of fruiting laterals will increase until the fan has reached its allotted limits. Then the tree will settle down to a steady-state condition with each fruiting lateral being replaced annually. If a main rib is considered to have become too old it can be removed and replaced by a shoot from near its base, which is extended every year until it has reached the required length. Provided that vigour can be maintained, the life of a peach can be very long because of the possibility of renewal of the ribs.

Peaches and nectarines do not have to be grown in heated houses, but if they are they should not be started into growth before the beginning of the year, and not before the tree has experienced as much low temperature as it is possible to give it by leaving ventilators fully open. Growth is started by providing a minimum night temperature of 7°C (*45°F*) until the flower buds are showing colour; then it is raised to 10°C (*50°F*). As light intensities increase the night temperatures may rise to 13°C (*55°F*) until the outside temperatures naturally exceed this level, and the thermostat should automatically shut off the artificial heat input. Daytime temperatures will, of course, be much higher than the night ones, but should be kept, by ventilation whenever possible, to not more than 9C° (*16F°*) above the night temperature. When outside temperatures have risen above 18°C (*65°F*) heat will not be required at all.

When the flowers are opening and are large enough to handle, the bunches are reduced to one single flower. When these are fully open, pollination with a rabbit's tail (or equivalent) is absolutely essential. As with vines, this is said to be best done during the middle of the day. After pollination, fertilised fruits begin to swell quite quickly. When they are as large as walnuts, they are thinned to a density of eleven per square metre (*one per square foot*). Thinning coincides with a period when the fruits stop swelling for several days while the shells of their stones differentiate and harden. After stoning, as it is called, the fruits swell rapidly and start to ripen.

Gardeners were formerly very zealous about 'damping down' which meant syringing the trees (with a hose pipe) two or three times a day, until ripening had commenced. This was done in part to help control red-spider mite. We now know that the control of red-spider achieved by this is minimal, and other benefits are difficult to identify. A humid atmosphere is necessary, but this can be achieved merely by keeping the soil surface moist. From starting the trees to the ripening of the fruits takes about five months.

A serious disease of peaches, highly specific to them, is peach leaf curl, caused by a fungus (*Taphrina deformans*). Measures taken to control it must be regarded as part of the routine cultivation of the fruit. Trees should be sprayed in February when the buds are swelling. If they are started very early spraying may be necessary even before this. The treatment is repeated in the autumn at leaf fall. The chemical used is a colloidal copper spray (see Appendix III), or the organo-sulphur compound Captan.

Figs

Figs were regularly grown in greenhouses in the great days of the private gardens, and in general the methods of cultivation described for grapes and peaches apply to them. They can, like peaches, be grown as fan trees against walls, as canopy fans 300 mm (*1 ft*) away from the glass, or with the fan crosswise in the house. Their root systems are rampant and are usually restricted by constructing a concrete base one metre (*3 ft*) deep in the soil, and building brick walls on it up to the soil surface. Provision is made in this for drainage so that what has been constructed is really a very large pot. The restriction of the root system which results prevents growth from becoming too rampant and throws the balance in favour of fruiting. The same was frequently done for vines. As so few amateurs will have greenhouse space available for figs, to grow one or two in pots is a more likely proposition.

Cuttings are taken in the middle of February and are made from ripened shoots about 200 mm (*8 in*) long, which should be straight and with a strong terminal bud. They are inserted into 75 mm (*3 in*) pots in either John Innes or peat compost and placed in a propagator or propagating case where a bottom heat of 26°C (*80°F*) is available. In such an environment

A young rooted cutting of a fig which is now just at the stage where it can be pruned to form a fan-shaped tree.

A very old fan-trained fig. This is probably at least a century old, and is still carrying regular crops of figs.

rooting takes place in about four weeks. Once rooted they are removed and placed on the greenhouse staging in a temperature not allowed to fall below 15°C (*60°F*). When the pots are full of roots, which should be in May, the young plants are re-potted in 250 mm (*10 in*) pots where they will remain for four or five years, possibly longer. This means that they must be grown under a liquid-feeding régime, because slow-release fertilisers could not sustain them for this length of time.

The young plant is stopped at a height of 150 mm (*6 in*) and a horizontal incision is made immediately above each bud on the stem (the incision is through the rind only) and this will cause them to break into growth. At the end of the summer the compost is allowed to become much drier to assist in ripening the wood. In winter the laterals are shortened back to ripe wood.

The following spring the plants must be started into growth in exactly the same way as peaches and vines; any small figs which had formed the previous summer will swell and ripen. While this is happening new lateral growths will be growing and must be stopped at a suitable bud, leaving the shoot between 150 mm (*6 in*) and 250 mm (*10 in*) long. On these laterals a second crop of figs forms, which should ripen at the end of the summer, giving two crops per year. As this happens some laterals should be growing which will end the season with small figs on them; these will develop the following spring. Ultimately the plant becomes too large for the pot, and drastic cutting back is necessary. Alternatively one starts again with younger plants.

Flowers under glass

Chapter 21

Chrysanthemums

The genus *Chrysanthemum* comprises about one hundred species of annuals, perennials and sub-shrubs, and the Royal Horticultural Society's *Dictionary of Gardening* lists almost fifty as having horticultural merit. Included in the genus are such garden plants as pyrethrum, the marguerites, feverfew and moon daisies, and weeds such as the ox-eye daisy and corn marigold.

The name chrysanthemum by itself is always taken to mean the autumn-flowering chrysanthemum, *Chrysanthemum morifolium* (meaning mulberry-leaved). It is probably one of the oldest of garden plants, having been cultivated in China for as long as 2,500 years and in Japan for over 1,000 years. Although so ancient it was not successfully introduced to Europe until 1789 when it was brought to the South of France. It reached England in 1795 and soon became one of the most popular flowers in cultivation, becoming affectionately known as the 'chrysanth' or 'mum'.

One of the most important things to understand about the chrysanthemum is that it is a short-day plant; that is to say, it normally cannot initiate the development of flowers until the length of the day is less than $14\frac{1}{2}$ hours. Once this has come about, flower buds develop and will open from 9 to 14 weeks later, depending upon the response-group in which the cultivar is placed, and the minimum night temperature it experiences.

In the south of England the length of the day becomes less than $14\frac{1}{2}$ hours by the middle of August, a few days later in northern England and later still in Scotland. In the south of England, starting from 14 August:

> a 9-week cultivar should flower by 16 October
> a 10-week cultivar should flower by 23 October
> an 11-week cultivar should flower by 30 October
> a 12-week cultivar should flower by 7 November
> a 13-week cultivar should flower by 14 November
> a 14-week cultivar should flower by 21 November

This will happen quite dependably provided a night temperature of 15.5°C (*60°F*) is maintained, at least for the first five or six weeks after 14 August, and never less than 13°C (*55°F*) thereafter. As the temperature in the British Isles in August is likely to be at least 15.5°C (*60°F*) chrysanthemums are sure to initiate their flower buds satisfactorily, but their subsequent development may be slowed down due to lower temperatures and poor light intensities. It is not uncommon to find in northern England and Scotland 13-week and 14-week cultivars not coming into flower until Christmas time, or even early January. Those who wish to avoid such a situation should not grow 13-week and 14-week cultivars such as 'Friendly Rival', 'American Beauty' and the 'Shoesmiths' unless they can provide the necessary temperature.

This basic knowledge about the physiology of the chrysanthemum plant gives some valuable guidance about its cultivation: in fact this knowledge has been exploited by the commercial grower to the extent that he is able, by manipulating the length of the day, and precisely controlling the temperature, to have chrysanthemums flowering in his greenhouses on virtually any day of the year he may choose.

The number of weeks from flower-bud initiation to flowering is constant for any cultivar if grown in optimum conditions, and is called its 'response-group'. Response-groups 9, 10, and 11 provide the amateur with most of his cultivars. The response-group classification supersedes terms such as 'early', 'mid-season' and 'late' chrysanthemums. At this point it is necessary to make a careful distinction between early cultivars, i.e. those in response-groups 9 and 10, and early-flowering chrysanthemums – a distinct group which flower in the open in August and September, being able to initiate flower buds in longer days. They come into the greenhouse only for over-wintering and propagation, and so will not be considered here, because their treatment in this respect is no different from that of the other cultivars.

Chrysanthemums are also classified according to the type of flower they produce:

1. Incurved In these the florets (the correct term for what are wrongly called petals) are all regularly incurved so that the bloom takes on the shape of a globe.
2. Reflexed In these types the outer florets curve downwards while the inner ones tend to incurve, thus giving a more flattened type of head.
3. Incurving These have irregular incurved petals giving a sort of mop-head. These were known formerly as Japanese varieties and are still known among enthusiasts as 'Japs'.
4. Anemone-flowered These are more like singles except that the disc florets form a central mass of tubes giving the so-called pin-cushion effect.
5. Pompons These have small button-like flowers and are often planted out for bedding purposes.
6. Singles These have a central disc and not more than five rows of ray florets at the periphery.
7. There are some trailing cultivars also available. These are mainly the decorative type known as 'cascade' chrysanthemums.

Enthusiasts who wish to show chrysanthemums have to familiarise themselves with the way each of these seven groups is sub-divided for show purposes.

The chrysanthemum is a popular plant for the amateur. Its heat demands are not excessive, and you can undertake its propagation and management without undue difficulty or special provisions. Nevertheless there are several methods of procedure from rooting the cutting to when the flowers are fully open. In the account that follows some of these will be outlined.

Cuttings

The best point to start is when the flowers have been cut, as for the chrysanthemum this divides one season from the next. We will assume that the old plants are in pots and that they have been cut down to leave a stem about 150 mm (*6 in*) long. According to the response-group, this can be any time from the end of October to the end of December. Cuttings can be struck from January until March, but with earlier propagation a longer season of growth is provided and sturdier plants result. Whatever the time when the cuttings are taken, the old plants, called 'stools', can remain in their pots. They should be kept at a low temperature, preferably 4.5 °C (*40° F*), at which they will be protected from frost yet not encouraged to break into growth too quickly. The chrysanthemum is almost hardy in the British Isles: in fact some cultivars will survive in the open in all but the harshest winters. Its growth pattern is that when it reaches maturity, or shortly afterwards, it starts to produce shoots from the base of the stem, both above and below the soil, and it is these which form the cuttings from which next year's crop will arise. During this period of waiting, the stools in their pots are packed close together in a place where they will get the maximum amount of available light. Even in the coldest season, attacks from greenfly, thrips and leaf miners must be taken seriously and dealt with at the very first sign.

Cuttings are detached from the stool with a sharp knife before they have become too long. Short-jointed slender cuttings seem to give better results than fat ones. They are trimmed to a length of about 50 mm (*2 in*). It is quite unnecessary to prepare the cutting by trimming away any leaves to give a length of stalk for insertion into the compost, or to cut the stem back to a joint, or as gardeners always say, a 'node'. Chrysanthemum cuttings root very easily in 50 mm (*2 in*) of compost on an open bench. The compost can be in trays of wood or plastic, or in pots, or preferably in half-pots, and can consist of John Innes Potting Compost No 1, the GCRI loamless compost, or a proprietory peat one. There is much to be said for a peat–fertiliser mix without sand. As the amateur will be propagating only small numbers of plants, he is probably best advised to use 140 mm ($5\frac{1}{2}$ *in*) half-pots, inserting five cuttings in each, equally spaced around their peripheries. It is most important that the pot is labelled with the name of the cultivar: memory fades very quickly and confusion will arise if cultivars become mixed. After insertion the cuttings are thoroughly watered and placed on the greenhouse staging. They are not watered again until roots have formed, which should be from three to four weeks later, depending on temperature. It is not necessary to cover the early batches of cuttings with polythene, for although they will wilt to begin with, they will soon recover and become turgid in winter, when the nights are long. If cuttings are not taken until March, when the days are brighter and the nights shorter, covering with polythene will be an advantage. While heat is not absolutely essential for rooting, best results come if the cutting is kept at a night temperature of 7.5 °C (*45° F*). In such conditions they should be rooted and ready for the next step in about four weeks. If they are being rooted in a cold frame or cold house they must be protected from frost by covering at night. In a greenhouse, newspaper placed directly over them is most effective. In frames, hessian is normally laid over the glass and weighted down.

Cuttings taken in January should have developed sufficiently by early March to be transferred to pots. The normal system is to pot rooted cuttings into 75 mm (*3 in*) pots, then about four weeks later to transfer them to 115 mm ($4\frac{1}{2}$ *in*) pots and then in about a further four weeks into the 'final' pot which is the large 250 mm (*10 in*) size. It would be quite a simple matter to leave out the intermediate pot and go straight from the 75 mm (*3 in*) size into the final pot, which might result in a somewhat 'softer' plant than is traditionally preferred; but the overriding consideration is

Transfer to pots

that of space. This is because the young plants must be kept in a cold frame until their final potting so that, while they are grown in as hardy conditions as possible, the facility for protecting them from harsh weather is always available. On balance, then, the traditional practice of using three sizes of pot is the most convenient.

Peat composts are quite suitable for growing chrysanthemums, although John Innes is perhaps easier to manage. The important decision to be made is whether a liquid feeding or a slow-release fertiliser system is to be used. Liquid feeding might theoretically give better results, but slow-release fertilisers enable far easier management to be carried out. For the first and intermediate pots the '3–4 month formulation' of slow-release fertiliser should be mixed with the compost in place of the normal fertiliser additives strictly in accordance with the manufacturer's instructions. The same applies to the potting compost for the final pots, except that the '8–9 month formulation' is used. If liquid feeding is used the normal fertiliser additives should be sufficient to support the plants throughout their sojourn in the 75 mm (*3 in*) pots and the 115 mm (*$4\frac{1}{2}$ in*) pots, but nevertheless they should be kept under close surveillance. If there is the slightest sign of hardening of the tissue or paling of their fresh green colour, liquid feeding should start forthwith. The feed to use is the 2 : 1 nitrogen/potash feed at a dilution of 1 in 200.

In traditional chrysanthemum growing in the past a great deal of energy was expended in ramming the compost very firm in the final pots. This is no longer considered necessary, as overhead watering of the pots soon brings about the necessary degree of consolidation.

The compost for final pots was formerly always made from unsieved chopped loam. This made sense then, because when compost was rammed solid, almost to the point of cracking the pot, a chopped chunky compost was more likely to retain some degree of air-filled porosity than a more finely sieved compost. Today it is considered that loam sieved to 10 mm (*$\frac{3}{8}$ in*) will mix more intimately with the peat, sand and fertiliser additives than would very coarse material. With peat composts there is no choice, as the peat will already have been granulated.

Young chrysanthemums should be ready for their final pots in May or early June. They leave the cold frames where they were formerly lodged and move to the 'standing ground'. This used to be an area of clinker on which the pots were placed until they were returned to the greenhouse in September. The purpose of a clinker-covered standing ground was to provide an area with a freely draining surface, abandoned by earthworms weed-free and clean to walk on. As clinker is no longer available and is not efficient anyway, the amateur must find a different way of providing summer accommodation for his chrysanthemums. The best suggestion is to cover an area of soil with 200-gauge black polythene, spread a layer of fine sand over it, and finally to stab it here and there with a garden fork to provide some drainage holes through the plastic.

The pots are placed in a row at least 450 mm (*18 in*) apart. If a second row is needed it should be 600 mm (*2 ft*) away from the first. Shortly after arrival on the standing area each pot has to be provided with a long cane, the top of which is secured to an overhead wire to prevent the pot blowing over. Many of the cultivars will have had to have been staked with a short cane while in the intermediate-size pots. Watering is most easily done by means of a trickle irrigation line, and at all times the compost in the pots should be kept as near to container capacity as possible.

As chrysanthemums grow they have to be stopped or pinched, a procedure which is relatively straightforward, but often seems somewhat mysterious to the amateur. The following explanation should help:

Stopping and flowering

1. The young rooted cutting, left to itself, grows for several weeks as a single-stemmed plant until
either (a) at its tip the stem develops a flower bud which instead of swelling remains the same size for a time and then drops off. At the same time side shoots form on the upper part of the stem below the bud,
or (b) the stem does not form a blind bud, but goes on growing until ultimately it begins to 'feather', that is, side shoots begin to appear on it.

In the first case the blind flower bud is called the *break bud* and the side shoots which surround it and continue the growth of the plant are called *breaks* or *lateral growths*; the plant is said to have made a *natural break*.

It will be clear that, in the case of those cultivars which produce a break bud, this cannot develop into a flower because of the long-day conditions which will exist at the time.

In the second case, the appearance of the 'feathers' indicates to the grower that the plant should be *stopped* by the removal of the growing point of the stem, just the tip of unfolded leaves. This stopping stimulates the feathers to develop into lateral branches, and is called making an *anticipated natural break*.

2. After the natural or anticipated natural break, the breaks or laterals continue their growth until they terminate in fully developed flower buds which are called *first crown buds*. A very large number of chrysanthemums are flowered on first crown buds. The first crown bud may be surrounded by leafy shoots or by other flower buds. In the latter case, the first crown bud is also a *terminal bud* and so are those surrounding it. The formation of terminal buds means that the cultivar in question is not capable of further vegetative growth.

If a cultivar is to be flowered on the first crown bud, then all the surrounding flower buds or leafy shoots must be removed, a procedure known as *disbudding* or *securing the bud*. If the first crown bud is also a terminal bud, and if it and all the flower buds around it are allowed to open, the resulting head of flowers is known as a *spray*.

It is, in fact, common practice to remove the crown bud from a spray fairly early to encourage even development of the surrounding buds.

3. If the first crown bud is surrounded by leafy growths and is removed together with all those leafy growths except the second one down, this will grow on for some time and ultimately terminate in a flower bud. This is called *running-on* and is a procedure adopted with many cultivars.

4. If, after a natural or anticipated natural break, the number of laterals is reduced to three or four, the removal of the others is called *counting down*. If these remaining laterals are allowed to develop for a time and then have their growing tips removed, in many cultivars this will result in the development of further laterals, which if allowed to continue their growth will produce flower buds. Such buds produced as a result of two stops (or one natural break plus a second stop) are called *second crown buds*. There is no real difference between a second crown bud and a bud produced as a result of running-on other than the timing of the second stop. Many cultivars are flowered on second crown buds, either because on first crown buds the flower is too coarse or too full, or because the stem is not long enough. It might also be that with a second crown bud a more intense colour is obtained.

5. Most cultivars of chrysanthemum are capable of carrying a dozen blooms. If they are to flower on first crown buds they are counted down to this number of laterals after the natural or anticipated natural break. If the required number of laterals has not been produced then the number can be increased by stopping the top three laterals at their first pair of leaves. Each will then produce two sub-laterals giving in all three extra shoots. If this is done as soon as possible, all the laterals will flower at the same time.

6. When chrysanthemums are grown for exhibition at shows and very large flowers are required, it may be necessary to count down the number of laterals to six or three or whatever number experience has shown to be best.

To summarise, the possibilities are as follows:

a. natural break – count down – flower on first crown buds;
b. natural break – count down – run-on – flower on second crown buds;
c. natural break – count down – second stop – flower on second crown buds;
d. anticipated natural break – count down – flower on first crown buds;
e. anticipated natural break – count down – run-on – flower on second crown buds;
f. anticipated natural break – count down – second stop – flower on second crown buds.

When growing a well-known cultivar it is usually possible to get information from catalogues or from other gardeners as to the stopping procedure favoured for it. With an unknown cultivar it is possible, provided that the stopping procedure is understood, to find by experiment which of the six possibilities best suits it.

The following short list of old-established cultivars gives some idea of stopping programmes:

Variety	First stop	Second stop	Flowering date
Ada Stevens	Natural break	run-on	mid-November
American Beauty	20th April	15th June	mid-December
Balcombe Flame	Natural break	——	3rd week October
Crenza	12th May	16th June	1st week November
Finale	8th June	——	3rd week November
Friendly Rival	8th June	——	2nd week December
Shirley Late Red	Natural break	run-on	mid-November
Sussex Bronze	10th May	12th June	3rd week November

Chrysanthemums are rehoused in September before night temperatures have fallen too low. It is very easy because of their hardiness to be misled into thinking that there is no urgency about bringing them in from the standing-out area. Indeed, they will survive, but the more low temperatures they experience the more will flowering be delayed.

An alternative to the method described is to pot the rooted cuttings into biodegradable pots and plant them, in due course, into the final pots. Another is to use biodegradable pots and plant them in the garden, and then to lift the plants into the greenhouse in September. This is a method that has been widely used by commercial growers for October-flowering cultivars, but it can be regarded only as a rough-and-ready method quite unsuited to the production of high-quality blooms, which is bound to be the desire of the amateur who has laboured with his plants all through the year.

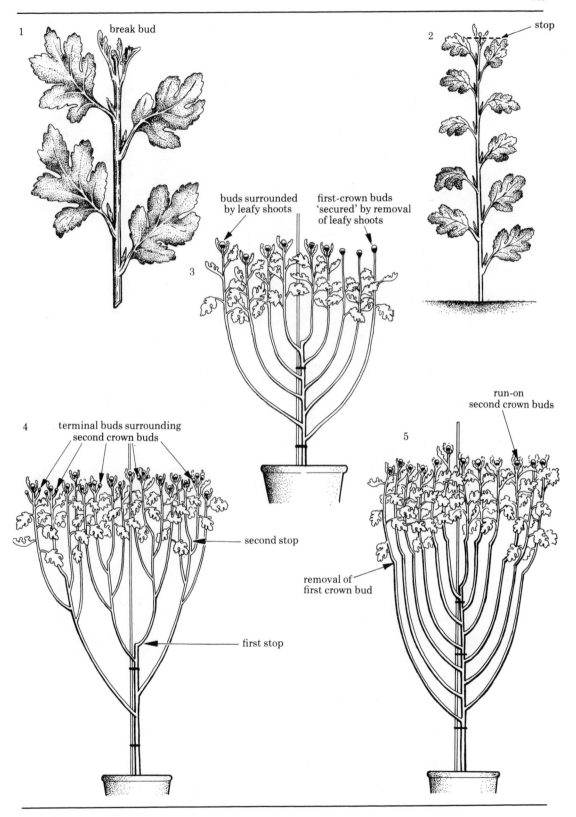

1 break bud

2 stop

3 buds surrounded by leafy shoots

first-crown buds 'secured' by removal of leafy shoots

4 terminal buds surrounding second crown buds

second stop

first stop

5 run-on second crown buds

removal of first crown bud

Decorative pot plants	Chrysanthemums do not necessarily have to be grown for the production of high-quality blooms for cutting, but instead can be grown as decorative pot plants for display. There are two ways of doing this: to produce dwarf plants in pots, or to produce large specimen plants in pots.

Dwarf plants in pots must not be confused with the 'all-the-year-round' dwarf pot chrysanthemums which are produced commercially by day-length control and by the use of chemical growth-retardants. The amateur can do this if he wishes, but the procedure is exacting and extremely costly unless large-scale production is planned. The traditional method is to take cuttings in late April or early May from decorative cultivars in the 9- and 10-week response-groups. 'Blanche Poitevene' is an example of an old-fashioned one of this type, and 'Princess Anne' and its sports (see Chapter 30 for an explanation of 'sports') an example of a modern one.

Three cuttings are spaced out around the periphery of a 75 mm (*3 in*) pot, and when rooted are transferred, as though they were one single plant, into a 150 mm (*6 in*) pot. This will be in the early part of June. When they are established a week or two later, each cutting is stopped by the removal of its growing tip. Two laterals are allowed to develop on each, so that six flowers on first crown buds should result, giving a very fine display that can be brought into the home.

A modification of the technique is to use a large exhibition cultivar and take the cuttings about a month earlier, in late March or early April. The cuttings are rooted individually in small biodegradable pots for preference and|transferred to 150 mm (*6 in*) pots. The plants are not stopped at all, but have all their side shoots removed. In due course the break bud will appear, late enough to catch the short days; it should be secured. Such plants produce enormous blooms, up to 225 mm (*9 in*) in diameter.

Large specimen plants are produced by rooting cuttings as early as possible in order to give the plant the longest possible period of vegetative growth. They are, if available, rooted as early as late November, although December is more usual. The cuttings are rooted into 75 mm (*3 in*) pots, biodegradable if preferred, then transferred when ready to 150 mm (*6 in*) pots and ultimately into 250 mm (*10 in*) or even 300 mm (*12 in*) pots.

The young plant is stopped either at the natural break or by means of the anticipated natural break, and all the laterals, other than any that are weakly, are allowed to develop. These are stopped when 100–150 mm (*4–6 in*) long and the resulting sub-laterals again stopped when 100–115 mm (*4–4½ in*) long. This last stop must be given not later than the end of June so that there are at least six weeks left for vegetative growth before the plant passes into the flowering phase in mid-August. This system should produce a large bushy plant with flowers all around it. Not all cultivars respond to this treatment, but 'Blanche Poitevene' and 'Windsor Gold' are well-tried for the purpose.

Virus-free stocks	Chrysanthemums which are always propagated by cuttings (except when new varieties are being bred) are susceptible to a number of viral diseases. These tend to build up in stocks, and account for the disappearance of many once-popular cultivars. Heat therapy coupled with micro-propagation has enabled many of them to be rid of their viral diseases, and healthy stocks have become available. Unfortunately the cultivars which have been so treated are those suitable for the modern commercial methods of controlled flowering-date production. However, they include many excellent decorative and incurved cultivars.

Chapter 22

Dahlias

At first glance it might be thought that dahlias are in the same category as the chrysanthemums dealt with in Chapter 21. This is not the case, however, because dahlias are herbaceous perennials which undergo dormancy during the winter, breaking into fresh growth from the old stool in the following spring.

The genus *Dahlia*, like the genus *Chrysanthemum*, belongs to the daisy family Compositae. It was introduced into Britain in 1804 only nine years after the chrysanthemums; it includes only about twelve species. The garden dahlias, which run into thousands of distinct cultivars, are thought to be mostly derived from *Dahlia juarezii* and *Dahlia rosea* and their hybrids, but in all probability other species are involved. So variable is the garden dahlia that the British National Dahlia Society divides it into at least eleven sections or series. There are singles, decoratives, pompons, cactus-flowered, anemone-flowered and so on, often sub-divided according to size.

Whatever the type, all need the same kind of cultivation and all are overwintered and propagated in the same way. They are easily raised from seed, but do not come true to type. Cultivars have to be maintained by vegetative propagation, with the inevitable result that stocks become infected with viral diseases, so that cultivars of great beauty and immense popularity disappear from cultivation in the course of time. It is now possible to rid cultivars of these diseases, but it adds greatly to their cost; so every grower of dahlias should inspect his plants for signs of viral disease throughout the summer. There are four diseases commonly found: spotted wilt, mosaic, ringspot and streak. Mosaic is probably the commonest and most dramatic in its effect. Whichever virus is causing the trouble, its presence shows up readily enough in the loss of vigour and stunted appearance of affected plants. These should be 'rogued' out and burned as soon as their presence is detected, because they are a source of infection to all other healthy plants. These diseases are spread by aphids, so the control of these is a deterrent to the spread of viruses. Unfortunately the eventual appearance of viral disease is virtually inevitable, so that roguing remains the chief weapon of control.

Dahlias are left for the enjoyment of their autumn flowers until the first frost suddenly blackens them and desiccates their foliage. They are then cut down to leave a few inches of stem and lifted for overwintering of the stools. After lifting, it is most desirable to wash them absolutely clean of soil and to ensure that they are thoroughly dry. Those without a greenhouse can store them in this condition in a dry frost-proof place until they start to sprout in the spring. The young shoots come from the base of the old stem, not from the tubers. Dahlia tubers are root tubers and cannot produce buds (botanists call them 'adventitious buds') as can the roots of

Overwintering and propagation

An overwintered dahlia tuber (or 'stool') in the springtime. This has been overwintered in a box of moist peat, and young shoots can be seen arising from the bases of the old stems — not, it will be noted, from the root tubers which are merely food storage organs with no capacity to produce adventitious buds.

many other plants. They are, therefore, quite useless for propagation, as they serve only for storing food. If stools are overwintered in the manner just described they can be planted out in the garden in May with the hope that there will not be a late frost to cut them back.

If the stock is to be increased, careful dissection of the stool is necessary so that each piece has a portion of stem with a shoot on it. For efficient propagation the method is to pack the washed stools into a box, or boxes, bedding them in moist (as opposed to wet) peat. Labelling is important at this stage to prevent muddling of the various cultivars. The stools should have the old stem just protruding above the peat. A wise precaution is to dust them with Benomyl/Thiram dust before boxing, and then to dust the surface after boxing, as a preventative against rots which may attack the tubers while they are dormant. As an alternative HCH/Captan dust can be used; this has insecticidal as well as fungicidal properties. The stools are kept in the greenhouse throughout the winter, and the only requirement is that the environment should be frostproof; 4.5 °C (*40°F*) is an adequate temperature. It is, in fact, common practice to keep boxes of dahlia stools under the greenhouse staging.

In February a temperature of 15.5 °C (*60°F*) will cause the stools to send up shoots, which are used as cuttings. When this happens the boxes can be brought out into full light and watered thoroughly once. Thereafter sprinkling the surface should suffice. Each shoot is detached when it has produced two pairs of leaves. They are potted preferably into 75 mm (*3 in*) biodegradable pots and placed in a propagator or propagating case until they are rooted, which should be within about three weeks. Where propagating space is limited the cuttings can be placed in a tray and potted when rooted. Although this saves space the potting-up process delays the development of the plant by a few days.

Once established in their pots and growing well, the plants should be moved to a cold frame. In the normal course of events this is unlikely to be before the middle of April. In the frames they are at first protected by the glass lights, and ventilated during the day. By May the lights are removed altogether during the day and only replaced at night if a clear sky should threaten a frost. Dahlias grow apace when in their pots and quickly harden, but they will starve unless liquid feeding is commenced, or unless slow-release fertilisers have been used in the potting compost. Starved plants, when planted out into their final positions, can take two or three weeks to recover: this represents lost flowering time. Although dahlias are marvellous plants for late summer and autumn displays, they often give their best blooms much earlier. They can be helped to do this by ensuring that they do not suffer checks to their growth during the propagation and growing-on stages.

Chapter 23

Spring bulbs

Spring bulbs can be made to flower in greenhouses weeks before their natural season and so provide bright colour in an otherwise dull period. Daffodils (*Narcissus*), hyacinths and tulips come first to mind, but there are others such as bulbous irises, *Muscari* (Grape hyacinth), *Chionodoxa*, *Scilla* (the bluebells) and *Ornithogalum*. The crocus, although not a bulb but a corm, and similarly freesia, could be added to the list.

Forcing procedures

The procedure for 'forcing' bulbs follows a consistent pattern with relatively minor variations for each of the different kinds. They are bought as soon as they become available in the shops — late August or early September – and stored in a cool place, that is to say somewhere where the temperature does not exceed 13°C (*55°F*), until they can be dealt with at the end of September, when the outside temperatures fall.

When this has come about the bulbs are put into containers in a suitable growing medium and are placed out of doors covered over with soil, sand or peat. Then they are soaked with water and left until November and December. By this time they will have developed extensive root systems, able to take up water freely, and the shoot will be 50–75 mm (*2–3 in*) long with the flower bud through the 'neck' of the bulb. In this position they are poised ready to flower, and if brought into a greenhouse (or the home) they will grow rapidly and come into bloom.

The bulbs, if subjected to certain treatment when in their dormant period, can submit to the forcing treatment somewhat sooner, and will respond to it so well that, if brought into a heated greenhouse, they can be in flower by Christmas.

A dormant bulb contains embryonic flowers enfolded in embryo leaves.

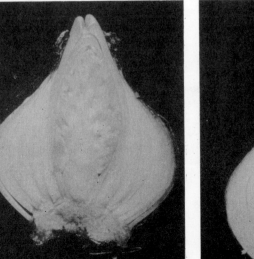 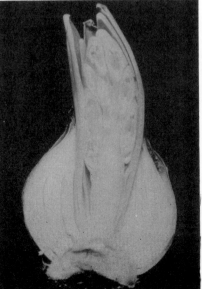

Left: a longitudinal section through a hyacinth bulb where the forthcoming inflorescence is fully developed but not yet emerged from the bulb. *Right*: in this case the embryo inflorescence has elongated so that it is through the neck of the bulb. This is the correct stage for bringing the bulb out of the 'plunge' and placing it in a warm, moist environment where it will rapidly develop into full flower.

As dormancy nears its end these embryonic flowers develop to the point where all their parts have become clearly differentiated and await the onset of spring, so that flowering can be as rapid as possible. A bulb is one form of adaptation for surviving winter, so this pattern of growth and development can be seen to be well suited to a climate where wet and warm springs are followed by hot dry summers, autumnal rains, and then snow cover during winter. In such a climate the time for growth and flowering is the spring and early summer; late summer and autumn are used for internal development and preparation for the future.

With this knowledge available, it was discovered in the 1920s and 1930s that if bulbs are lifted when the foliage has died down, put into an environment where temperature can be accurately controlled, and then subjected to warm treatment, the differentiation of the flower parts within them is much quicker than if the bulb were still in cooler soil. After the warm temperature, cooler treatment is necessary to prevent growth of roots and shoots, and consequent loss of moisture, taking place during the rest of the storage period.

This forwarding, during storage, of the internal development of the bulb is technically described as 'vernalisation', although in the trade the bulbs are described as 'treated' or 'prepared'; they are naturally somewhat more expensive than untreated ones.

The necessity for keeping lifted bulbs in cool conditions until 'plunging' is obvious in the case of vernalised bulbs. Prepared hyacinths are particularly sensitive to high temperatures before plunging and have been known to fail altogether after exposure to them. It seems that the growth and development processes may be disturbed irreversibly.

The individual treatments given to each of the three main bulbs follow.

Narcissus

The bulbs are lifted from the fields in late June and early July and given various disinfection treatments to ensure they are free from pests and diseases.

a. Those required for flowering from mid-November to late December are given a temperature of 35°C (*95°F*) for five days, followed by 17°C (*62°F*) until the flower parts are fully developed. This is called 'Stage Pc'. (Pc stands for paracorolla which is the tissue from which the trumpet forms and which must be differentiated.) They are then stored at 9°C (*48°F*) for six weeks and then boxed.

b. Those required for flowering in late December and January are kept at 17°C (*62°F*) until Stage Pc is reached. This is ascertained by twice-weekly

The flower initials or primordia dissected from a *Narcissus* bulb. The fluted structure is called the paracorolla. This will in due course form the trumpet of the daffodil.

Narcissus bulbs in flower ready for ornamental use in a dwelling house or on the staging of a conservatory.

dissections and examinations of the bulbs. They are then stored at 9°C (*48°F*) for six weeks and then boxed.
c. For flowering in February and March they are stored at 17°C (*62°F*) from lifting until boxing in September.

a. For early flowering the bulbs, after lifting, cleaning and grading, are stored at 20°C (*68°F*) until the flowers within the bulb have developed to the point where the six stamens and their anthers are clearly visible on dissection. They are then stored at 17°C (*62°F*) until the remainder of the flower parts are visible; this takes from one to two weeks. From then until boxing they are stored at 9°C (*48°F*).
b. For January and February flowering they are stored at 20°C (*68°F*) as above, but thereafter at 17°C (*62°F*) until boxing.

Tulips

a. For Christmas flowering the bulbs are lifted in the middle of June and stored at 23°C (*73°F*) until the first whorl of stamens has developed which takes about 10 days, then at 30°C (*86°F*) for five weeks, then finally 17°C (*62°F*) until boxing.
b. For flowering in January and early February they are stored from lifting until mid-September at 25.5°C (*78°F*) then at 17°C (*62°F*) until boxing in October.

Hyacinths

In addition to the main bulbs, temperature treatments can also be given to bulbous irises, *Muscari armeniacum*, freesia corms and gladiolus corms, but it is unusual for amateur gardeners to be concerned with bulbs and corms so treated.

The description of these complicated treatments may well put the amateur off having anything to do with them. Indeed, it is hardly worth considering them unless the forcing temperatures required in mid-winter can be afforded. Commercial vernalised bulbs are freely available and not all that much more expensive.

Bulbs are often grown in the home in bulb-bowls containing bulb fibre. This is a mixture of peat, charcoal, lime and sometimes osmunda fern fibre, and is specially prepared and sold for the purpose. The fibre is thoroughly soaked, then all the excess moisture is squeezed out and the fibre is put into bowls ready for the bulbs to be bedded in. The bowls are placed in the dark somewhere until the shoots are showing, when they are brought into the light again for flowering when ready. As the containers do not, as a rule, have drainage holes, watering has to be done sparingly to avoid waterlogging at the bottom of the bowl.

Bulbs in the home

Although this method is traditional and popular, it rarely gives the best results, because it is difficult in a modern home to find a cool, damp environment, which the bulbs need while they are developing their root systems. If the bowls can be placed outdoors and covered with moist sand or peat, and protected from the rain by a sheet of 500-gauge black plastic (or even a sheet of corrugated iron or asbestos) until the end of November, so much the better. More satisfactory methods for those with a greenhouse are now described.

Narcissus

The genus *Narcissus* is divided into eleven divisions, of which ten are of garden origin, the products of many years of breeding and hybridisation. Most popular for forcing by amateur gardeners are varieties from Division 1, the Trumpet Narcissus, commonly called daffodils, of which 'Golden Harvest' and 'Magnificence' are among the best-known. Division 2, Large-Cupped Narcissus, commonly called narcissi, are next in popularity, and the varieties 'Carlton' and 'Fortune' are widely used. All the other groups can be forced but are less popular. Daffodils and narcissi are best forced in pots which are at least 115 mm ($4\frac{1}{2}$ *in*) deep.

It is usual to rest the bulbs on 50 mm (*2 in*) of peat and then add another 50 mm (*2 in*) of peat between and over them. Some people like to get more for their money and use a large pot with one tier of bulbs above the other. The first tier stands on a layer of peat as described above and is then completely covered with peat so that another tier of bulbs can be placed above the first. The bulbs in the pot can be quite close together; in fact, almost touching at their widest parts. The filled pots are then placed outdoors on a 50 mm (*2 in*) layer of peat or sand spread over a sheet of 200-gauge black polythene which has been slightly cambered to give free and rapid drainage. The pots are placed close together, covered with 125 mm (*5 in*) of peat and thoroughly soaked. This is called 'plunging' the bulbs. Soaking at weekly intervals, at least, is necessary if the weather is warm and if prepared bulbs have been used, so that the evaporation of the moisture will keep the bulbs cool. Once the outdoor temperature drops below 9°C (*48°F*) there is no further cause for concern. With untreated bulbs (or bulbs 'as lifted'), an initial soaking is essential, but thereafter further watering is needed only if the autumn is exceptionally sunny and dry.

Although it is less expensive to plunge bulbs into soil, peat and sand are much cleaner to use. Old peat coming from used modules, if rubbed through a coarse sieve, is quite satisfactory.

Whatever bulb is being plunged it is always a good idea to put a 13 mm ($\frac{1}{2}$ *in*) layer of sand on top of the filled containers as this greatly facilitates cleaning away the unwanted plunging material when the bulbs are brought into the greenhouse.

As already emphasised, *Narcissus* can be brought into the greenhouse when, but not until, the flower buds are through the necks of the bulbs. In the greenhouse they can be placed on the staging or the floor, and ideally need a temperature of 15°C (*60°F*).

At lower temperatures the flowers will develop more slowly. Pots from the plunge beds can, of course, be brought into the home and allowed to develop there. *Narcissus* are forced commercially for cutting, but the amateur is almost certainly growing his for display in the pot, which means that careful and unobtrusive staking with green rattan canes will be necessary. Watering must be frequent throughout the forcing period, but no liquid feeding is necessary. Forced bulbs can be planted in the garden as soon as flowering is over.

Tulips

Tulips, of which there are hundreds of cultivars, are classified into as many as 23 groups. The first three groups (*1* Duc van Tol tulips, *2* Single Early tulips and *3* Double Early tulips) constitute the 'Early Flowering Tulips', all of which can be forced. The next two groups (*4* Mendel tulips and *5* Triumph tulips) constitute the 'Mid-Season Flowering Tulips', all of which can also be forced. Groups *6–15* are the 'Late Flowering Tulips'; among these group *10*, Cottage tulips, are suitable for forcing. Groups *16–23*, the tulip species and their hybrids and varieties, are not normally forced.

While commercial growers force thousands of tulips every year for cut-flower production, they are otherwise not very good plants for ornamental display purposes. Single and Double Early tulips in groups 2 and 3 do make for attractive containers of short-stemmed flowers, whereas cultivars in the other groups are too tall, and even when staked are still not very attractive.

The bulbs are placed in containers so that they stand on about 75 mm (*3 in*) of peat. Amateurs will find it best to use half pots or pans as containers for tulips. The bulbs do not need to be covered, but the peat on which they stand must be covered by a layer of sand. They are plunged just like *Narcissus* bulbs.

They must not be brought into the greenhouse until the flower bud is through the neck of the bulb. It is not visible in the way that the *Narcissus* bud is, but can usually be detected by feeling the sprouts on the bulbs.

Information is available stating for each cultivar whether it is suitable for forcing, and, if so, the earliest date that forcing can normally commence. It is not possible to reproduce this list in full, but some examples of popular varieties are given in the table.

Name	Group	Earliest forcing dates
Duc van Tol	Duc van Tol	1 December
Bel Ami	Single Early	15 December
Couleur Cardinal	Single Early	25 January
Keizerkroon	Single Early	21 February
Sun-burst	Single Early	28 January
Mr Van de Hoef	Double Early	Not suitable
Peach Blossom	Double Early	Not suitable
Vurbaak	Double Early	5 January
Early Queen	Mendel	5 December
Krelage's Triumph	Mendel	15 December
Weber	Mendel	10 January
Bruno Walters	Triumph	15 January
Elmus	Triumph	15 January
Rijnland	Triumph	20 January
Campfire	Darwin	15 January
Demeter	Darwin	20 December
Niphetos	Darwin	20 January
Prunus	Darwin	15 January
Red Pitt	Darwin	5 January
Rose Copland	Darwin	25 December
William Pitt	Darwin	5 January

NB If the bulbs have been vernalised all these dates can be advanced by two weeks.

Once in the greenhouse the temperature is gradually raised to 21°C (*70°F*) to give the most rapid development. Lower temperatures, such as

15°C (*60°F*), cause the whole process to be slower, though sturdier plants result. The early flowering tulips are forced in the dark to make the stems longer for cutting, but this will not apply to the amateur. Tulips being forced in February and March need some shading, and must never be watered overhead, or spotting of the blooms is likely.

Most cultivars of tulips, if not all, grow very well in cold greenhouses, including plastic houses. They are planted in the soil and allowed to grow quite naturally. They require plenty of ventilation and one or two heavy waterings, and will produce excellent long-stemmed flowers for cutting.

The amateur gardener is likely to prefer to force the early flowering tulips grown in bowls and used for decoration in the greenhouse or home. They are much shorter than other kinds, and do not need staking.

Hyacinths

Hyacinths are such elegant plants that they can be grown as single specimens in pots for which purpose the 'top' size of bulb gives the best results. The largest bulbs or 'tops' are usually those of 180–190 mm (*7–7½ in*) in circumference, except for the yellow varieties where 160–170 mm (*6–6½ in*) is the largest size. Those in the next size down are suitable for planting three in a bowl or half-pot. Not all cultivars are suitable for forcing, and certainly not all are suitable for being 'prepared'. A short list of the tried and trusted favourites follows:

White
Arentine Arendsen
Eidelweiss
L'Innocence

Rose
Anna Marie
Early Beauty
Imperator
Pink Perle

Blue
Bismarck
Delft Blue
Dr Leiber
Ostara

Red
Garibaldi
Jan Bos
Tubergen's Scarlet

Yellow
Yellow Hammer

Orange
Orange Boven (late only)

Violet
Mauve Queen (late only)
Sir William Mansfield (late only)

Doubles
Ben Nevis (white)
Madame Sophie (white)

Plunging hyacinths out of doors is the same as for *Narcissus*, except that special care is needed to ensure that prepared bulbs do not experience temperatures above 17°C (*62.5°F*). This can usually be achieved by ensuring that the peat covering is always wet, so that evaporative cooling can take effect on sunny days.

The first batch of prepared bulbs is usually brought into the greenhouse at the end of November. The temperature starts at 13°C (*55°F*), then after two days it is gradually raised to 24°C (*75°F*). They are forced in darkness until the shoots are 100 mm (*4 in*) long, after which they complete their development in partial shade; in other words, they are shaded from any sunshine which might occur. They are watered daily using a can with a fine rose. High relative humidity is required in the forcing environment.

'Unprepared' bulbs can be brought in for forcing at any time after Christmas. Those started before the middle of February need darkness until the shoots are 100 mm (*4 in*) long, but after this time they will have reached the required length before being brought into the greenhouse. If the specified temperature cannot be maintained, flowering will be delayed.

Iris

Only the bulbous irises are suitable for forcing, and the amateur is much more likely to be attracted to the smaller species, such as *Iris histrio*, *Iris histrioides* and *Iris reticulata*, as these can be grown in bowls and half pots, to make very decorative displays. *Iris reticulata* has become very popular for this purpose in recent years.

The Dutch Iris (*Iris tingitana*) is of hybrid origin and is grown for cut flowers. It is a magnificent plant and has superseded the English Iris (*Iris xiphioides*) and the Spanish Iris (*Iris xiphium*) for this purpose. While it is also a good garden plant, under glass it is really only suitable for cutting.

The small species – such as *Iris reticulata* – grown in bowls and half pots are bought as dry bulbs and can be grown in peat composts. They do not need to be plunged, but can be kept in the greenhouse on the staging, where they will flower in due course at relatively modest temperatures around 12–15°C (*55–60°F*).

The bulbs of the Dutch Iris, which can be obtained 'pre-cooled' for early flowering, are best planted in the greenhouse soil so that they are not subsequently disturbed. They do not respond to high temperatures, 10°C (*50°F*) being the maximum that should be provided by heating. Because of this they are suitable for growing in cold greenhouses.

Muscari

Muscari armeniacum, the Grape Hyacinth, can easily be forced in pots and pans at a temperature of 15°C (*60°F*) to give very delightful displays. The flowers are also ideal for table decorations and corsage work. They can be purchased as pre-cooled bulbs, but as they grow very readily and spread in most gardens, they can be lifted for forcing when the leaves have died back. The largest bulbs are selected and placed close together on peat. They are covered so that they are just below the surface, leaving about 13 mm ($\frac{1}{2}$ *in*) for a covering of sand. They are then placed in the plunge bed until ready for forcing in the greenhouse after Christmas.

Crocus

Most of the spring-flowering garden crocuses have derived from *Crocus vernus*, and are available in a range of colours. For example:

'Remembrance'	Blue
'Vanguard'	Grey–mauve
'Jeanne D'Arc'	White
'Striped Beauty'	Blue on white

Yellow crocuses are not recommended for forcing.

The procedure is a simple one, the corms being treated in a similar manner to *Muscari*. They should not be brought into the greenhouse until the middle of January, nor given temperatures in excess of 13°C (*55°F*).

Chapter 24

Hardy plants for greenhouse display

Annuals

Annuals are plants which complete their life cycle in one season and contain within their ranks some of the most showy plants. In mild climates, like the British, annuals frequently germinate during the moist, warm days of autumn and overwinter as seedlings. In the spring they grow rapidly and flower early, often making more handsome plants than others of the same kind sown in the spring. This phenomenon can also be observed with common annual weeds. It has long been exploited by farmers and gardeners in their methods of cultivating certain crops, such as autumn-sown corn, beans, lettuces, and spinach.

One method of such exploitation which was widely practised by private gardeners, and which to a certain extent still is by public-parks gardeners, is that of sowing annuals in the autumn and overwintering them in pots in the greenhouse. As soon as the days lengthen in the spring, growth becomes rapid, and by early summer they are in flower. While all hardy annuals and half-hardy annuals respond to this treatment, some are more worthwhile than others; a short list includes the following:

1. *Antirrhinum majus* (F1 hybrids most suitable)
2. *Clarkia elegans* and *C. pulchella* (usually listed as *C. elegans* by seedsmen)
3. *Godetia amoena* and *G. grandiflora* (both together called godetia by seedsmen)
4. *Delphinium ajacis* and *D. consolida* – larkspur
5. *Matthiola incarna* – ten-week stock
6. *Lathyrus odoratus* – the sweet pea
7. *Salpiglossis sinuata* (F1 hybrids available)
8. *Schizanthus pinnatus*

The special attractions of the above method are threefold: first, seed is relatively inexpensive; secondly, the temperatures required in the greenhouse are low—in fact, no more than protection from frost is needed; and finally, a colourful display is available at a time when other flowers are in short supply.

The method of cultivation is quite straightforward: sowing takes place in the first few days of September, so that there is sufficient time for the seeds to germinate and be pricked-off before shortening days and falling temperatures cause growth to slow down. A small 75 mm (*3 in*) pot will normally supply all the seedlings that are required. It is necessary for the seedlings to be established by the beginning of October in the pots in which it is intended to flower them. These annuals are flowered in 150 mm (*6 in*), 175 mm (*7 in*) and even larger pots if so desired. They tend to grow quite tall, so the pot must be large enough to give them sufficient stability when they are fully grown. This is especially important when peat composts are being used, because they make the pot so light that it becomes top-heavy.

Pelletted seed used for raising plants under glass. The six peat blocks on the left each contain five pelleted onion seeds (multi-seeded blocks). The three blocks on the far left show the onion seeds covered with sand to keep them moist until they have germinated. The six peat blocks on the right contain single pelleted lettuce seeds; they will similarly be covered with a small quantity of sand but must be kept very cool until germination has taken place because of thermal dormancy.

The seedlings are pricked-out around the periphery of the pot in which they are to flower. The distance between each seedling will depend to some extent on its ultimate size, but somewhere in the region of 75 mm (*3 in*) is about right. There is a temptation to place an additional seedling in the middle of the pot, but this is inadvisable. The amount of watering required during the winter will be very small indeed, but once growth gets under way in the spring the need will increase rapidly.

There are other methods that can be followed. For example, *Antirrhinum*, *Clarkia* and *Godetia* seeds are available in pelleted form and can be sown singly in small pots (or preferably small peat blocks), overwintered in them and planted out into the larger pots as soon as they start to grow in the spring. Alternatively, seedlings can be pricked-out singly into 75 mm (*3 in*) pots for overwintering and then either flowered in these small pots as single plants, moved into 125 mm (*5 in*) pots to make larger single plants, or planted around the periphery of a larger pot.

Liquid feeding commences after rapid growth has started in the spring, using the 2 : 1 nitrogen to potash feed at the dilution rate of 1 in 200, applied with every watering (see Appendix II). This will produce magnificent plants, but equally good results can be obtained with slow-release fertilisers.

Annuals almost always require to be staked. This must be done well before the support is needed. One rattan or split cane is sufficient for single plants, but where the pot contains several plants the canes must be inserted around its periphery so that they all point regularly outwards. 'Green twist' is then tied round in tiers as required.

Sweet peas have been included on the list at the beginning of this chapter, although they are normally grown as flowers for cutting. If grown for display, the best procedure is to raise one plant in a 75 mm (*3 in*) pot, and to stop it in the usual way when it has made a few centimetres of growth. The plant's response to this is to produce about three laterals which in normal production are reduced, in the spring, to one only. When growing for display, all these can be left on the plant, which is transferred to a pot no smaller than 225 mm (*9 in*). The three laterals are trained in circular fashion around four canes inserted into the pot and pointing outwards. There is no need to remove the tendrils, as is done in conventional growing.

Stocks are also included in the list. As there are several kinds, note that the annual ten-week stock is intended. The Hanson 100 per cent double type is useful, because the genetic factor for double flowers is linked to that for the colour of the seed leaf; that is, double-flowered plants have pale seed leaves, while single-flowered ones have dark green leaves. Doubles can thus be readily identified and selected, and the disappointing consequence of a mixture of double and single flowers avoided.

Biennials

True biennials are plants which arise from seed and which grow only vegetatively in the first season; then, after exposure to lower temperatures in the winter, they flower in the following spring or early summer, after which they die. Some of the best examples are among the garden root vegetables: beet, parsnip and carrot. Among the flowering subjects are:

> *Campanula medium* 'Calycanthema' – Canterbury Bell
> *Campanula pyrimidalis* – Chimney Bellflower
> *Digitalis purpurea* – Foxglove
> *Matthiola incarna* – Brompton Stock

All these are hardy plants easily raised from seed, making excellent displays if flowered early in unheated greenhouses.

True biennials should not be confused with many plants which are in fact perennials, but which for convenience are treated as biennials, such as wallflowers which are useless for spring bedding after their first season of flowering, or Gaillardia and Sweet William which are short-lived and deteriorate after their first year. To confuse the question, most biennials will behave as annuals if subjected to low temperatures while in the seedling stage; for example, most varieties of red beet produce flowers (bolt) if they experience soil temperatures below 4.5°C (*40°F*) for any length of time. Such treatment, of course, results in useless plants or unsatisfactory flowers.

The biennials mentioned should all be sown in May or June in a cold greenhouse or frame, pricked-off into 75 mm (*3 in*) pots, and once established moved outside. They are transferred to the pot in which they are to flower in August, or earlier if their roots have filled the small pot.

Pots of the annual plant *Schizanthus*, sometimes called the 'poor man's orchid'. These plants have come from seeds which were sown in the autumn and which have been overwintered as seedlings under glass. With the onset of spring they have come rapidly into flower to provide a colourful indoor display. These plants require support, but not in the clumsy manner depicted in the photograph.

The campanulas need fairly large pots, as they make large plants and will topple over if the pot is too small. This warning has to be given repeatedly, because in these days of liquid feeding and slow-release fertilisers it is possible to grow large plants in small pots, in a way that would have seemed impossible a few years ago. Foxgloves also grow tall and need a 225 mm (9 in) pot with staking, while Brompton Stocks can be managed successfully in 125 mm (5 in) or 150 mm (6 in) pots, and will not need staking. Foxgloves, incidentally, are common enough in gardens as self-sown seedlings, but it is inadvisable to use these as they will almost certainly be the common purple type, whereas seedsmen's selections have a wider colour range and larger flowers.

Herbaceous perennials

Herbaceous perennials, strictly speaking, are plants with annual foliage and perennial rootstocks. This pattern of growth is a means of surviving the winter; one form of it has already been described in the case of bulbs (see page 120). With the onset of autumn the foliage dies down and the rootstock becomes dormant, deriving protection from its covering of soil, from the canopy of desiccated foliage, and often from a layer of snow. It is important that dormant plants should not start into growth before spring has arrived, and to prevent this happening they usually have a built-in mechanism which prevents growth occurring until certain conditions have been satisfied. It is often the case – as with rhubarb (see Chapter 26) – that a certain amount of exposure to cool temperatures must be experienced before dormancy is broken. Once this has come about, the worst of the winter should have passed, and the plant is poised to start into growth as soon as the temperature rises. This is true of virtually all hardy herbaceous perennials such as delphiniums, lupins, sunflowers, asters and so forth, but it does not apply to tender ones such as dahlias and potatoes, nor to sub-shrubs such as some of the chrysanthemums, which are treated by gardeners as though they were herbaceous plants. Incidentally, it is as well to draw a distinction between herbaceous perennials and perennial herbs such as lawn grasses, *Lilium candidum* and many hundreds of exotic plants which in their own habitat do not experience frost, and which, therefore, do not need an overwintering mechanism of the kind just described.

Having defined the term 'hardy herbaceous perennials', it is now possible to state that once these have had their dormancy overcome they may be forced into early flower in cool greenhouses. There is one further proviso: they must be 'long-day' plants, that is, those which flower in early and high summer; those like asters (Michaelmas daisies) which do not flower until the days are shortening do not respond satisfactorily to forcing.

As with annuals, many herbaceous perennials, though excellent border plants, are not sufficiently showy to be worth forcing for indoor display, but those which are include the following hardy garden plants:

Astilbe × arendsii
Delphinium – the hybrid border types
Primula polyanthus – the Polyanthus Primrose
Primula veris – the Cowslip
Primula vulgaris – the Primrose.

The Primrose and Cowslip behave as herbaceous plants in cold winters and as perennial herbs in mild ones.

Astilbes The hybrid *Astilbe × arendsii*, which has a number of cultivars, is regularly forced to flower in pots. Commercial growers market them in March and April. If these are purchased and established in the garden, they can be lifted and flowered in heated or unheated greenhouses. The method is to lift and pot the dormant roots, in October or November, into 125 mm (*5 in*) or 150 mm (*6 in*) pots. If sufficiently large the crowns may be divided, and in any event the roots may need a certain amount of trimming in order that they can be accommodated in the pots. The pots are placed out on a standing area, without any protection, until January, by which time they will be in a condition suitable for forcing. The forcing temperature is 18–20°C (*65–70°F*), at which it takes up to twelve weeks to bring them into flower. In unheated greenhouses it takes perhaps four weeks longer; such plants will flower in late April, and will probably look much better than the plants forced at higher temperatures.

Astilbes are very popular in the USA where it is common for growers to treat the dormant stools with warm water, immersing them for 20 minutes at a temperature of 44–44.5°C (*110–112°F*). This is said to reduce the forcing period by as much as two weeks with certain cultivars. The explanation of this is presumably concerned with the biochemical processes controlling dormancy.

Delphiniums make superb plants for display in May if grown in large pots, 225 mm (*9 in*) or 250 mm (*10 in*). Although there are named cultivars of delphinium, it is normal to raise delphiniums from seed which is sown in the summer, preferably in a container kept in a cold frame or greenhouse. The seedlings are transferred to a 75 mm (*3 in*) pot as soon as possible, and when they are established they are placed in an open frame until the following spring. Then they are planted in the garden where they will flower the following summer. This provides a means of identifying the best plants which can then be selected for forcing. In the autumn such plants (which will still not be too large) can be potted into the large pots for forcing. These are kept on a standing area until March when they are brought into an unheated greenhouse. Provided they are kept well watered, they will flower early in May. Long canes are required for staking them.

Another method of obtaining plants for pots from established clumps is by means of cuttings. These are obtained by tearing young shoots from the outside of the stool in the early spring when they are 50–75 mm (*2–3 in*) long. Obtained in this way they will have a heel, whereas if cut with a knife the stem is likely to be hollow. They can be struck in 75 mm (*3 in*) pots, placed in a cold frame or greenhouse, and flowered the same year as single spikes.

Polyanthus, primroses and cowslips These plants make most delightful pot plants and have the advantage that they are both easy and cheap to produce: among the primroses, for example, the F1 hybrid 'Sutton's Colour Magic' is superb for the purpose; there are similar F1 hybrids among the polyanthus such as 'Sutton's Lemon Punch' and 'Spring Promise'. The cowslip can be obtained in mixed colours, and although demure compared with its two relatives has its own special charm.

For flowering in pots, all should be sown in April in a cold greenhouse. When germinated they are transferred to 75 mm (*3 in*) pots, and as soon as established they are moved to a standing area in the open. The compost should have slow-release fertiliser added at the appropriate rate, so that the pots will require only regular and frequent watering until growth slows down in the autumn. During the winter they are transferred to larger containers, 140 mm ($5\frac{1}{2}$ in) half pots being excellent for the purpose. They are then brought back into the greenhouse and placed on the staging. Provided they are kept moist and cool, they will progress well, and flowers can be expected in abundance in March.

Many shrubs, particularly deciduous ones, may be brought into flower early in greenhouses. Best known of all is *Hydrangea macrophylla*, which is often wrongly called *Hydrangea hortensia* by gardeners because many of the best-known varieties are, in fact, forms of the cultivar *Hydrangea macrophylla* 'Hortensia'. The hydrangea is a superb display-plant because what pass for flowers are, in fact, coloured bracts which have a long life. They appear long before the very small flowers open, and then persist until after they have finished.

    The hydrangea is propagated from inter-nodal cuttings,* about 75 mm– 100 mm (*3–4 in*) long, taken as soon as available. Commercial raisers bring stock plants into a heated greenhouse in January in order to get early cuttings which will be rooted by April, and which then have a whole season of growth before them, so that they make large plants for forcing the following spring.

Shrubs

*where the cut is made across the stem midway between a pair of leaves

A young hydrangea plant just coming into flower. It will be noted that one of the shoots is blind — that is to say it is not going to produce flowers — and it is this kind of shoot which is usually selected to make a cutting. Reservations are expressed about this practice it may be that plants with a high proportion of blind shoots could be produced by propagating from blind shoots.

The cutting, as soon as it is established in a 75 mm (*3 in*) pot, has its growing tip removed, and the resulting two shoots are themselves pinched when they have formed a pair of leaves. The process is repeated a third time, and selected shoots from the third tier of laterals may be pinched in an attempt to produce plants capable of carrying twelve heads. In June or late May the young plants are moved from 75 mm (*3 in*) pots to 150 mm (*6 in*) pots in which they will flower. Hydrangeas are calcifuges (lime-haters), and do not grow well in compost where the amount of lime present has increased owing to watering with hard water. The amateur may not be able to start as early as the commercial grower, and without the advantages of heat may not get shoots large enough for cutting until April or May. Late cuttings are best not stopped at all, but instead should be allowed to run-up to give one single head. Such plants can be cut back after flowering to make larger plants for the following year. Some debate exists about the best source of cuttings. At one time it was customary to use blind shoots for cuttings, but now this is thought to encourage the formation of further blind shoots. When using flowering shoots, the tiny flower head is removed, which means that the cutting has already had one stop. If the cuttings are late, and single-stemmed plants are wanted, one of the laterals should be removed while still small.

Plants from cuttings taken in February and March can be forced eleven to twelve months later, while those rooted later, unless grown as single-stemmed plants, will not be ready until some twenty months have elapsed.

Hydrangeas require much feeding, and while slow-release fertilisers are excellent, the plants will remain in the pots longer than the supply of nutrients will last, so that liquid feeding has to take over in due course. Plants bought when in flower may be forced again the following year in a slightly larger pot (or even the original pot) provided that they are maintained on a continual liquid-feeding programme.

Whatever the age or size of the plant, the hydrangea, as a hardy plant, should be kept outside on a standing area throughout the summer and during the autumn. Protection is required only if severely cold weather should occur, as this will destroy the flower initials within the dormant buds and only blind shoots will result. Conversely, if temperatures over 10°C (*50°F*) persist for any length of time after the plant has ripened, flower-bud formation may be inhibited. Normal practice, therefore, is to bring the plants, in late October, into cold-houses or cold-frames.

The earliest time for forcing is mid-December; this produces flowers at the end of March. However, it is more usual, and for the amateur more advisable, to start forcing after Christmas in January or February. When forcing starts, the plants are watered and the temperature is slowly raised to 15°C (*60°F*), at which they will develop satisfactorily. Once well into growth, the procedure can be speeded up by raising the temperature to 18°C (*65°F*), but this is not essential. Temperatures above this cause soft growth and should be avoided at all costs, particularly as unnecessarily high temperatures mean higher fuel bills.

Hydrangeas range in colour from carmine through pink to white. Many pink varieties in acid soils become deep blue in colour, and this fact is exploited in their cultivation by treating them with aluminium sulphate to make them blue. A solution is made by dissolving 3 grams of aluminium sulphate in one litre of water ($\frac{1}{2}$ *oz to 1 gallon*), and this solution is watered onto the plants at fortnightly intervals. Alternatively, aluminium sulphate can be added to the liquid feed and thus applied at every watering. The amount that has to be added to the stock solution is very small – 0.33 grams per litre (*0.055 oz/gallon*). The best way of adding such a small amount is to dissolve 40 grams of aluminium sulphate in one litre of water, and then add 5 ml of this solution to one litre of the liquid-feed stock solution.

Some varieties that are suitable for 'blueing' are:

'Holstein'	'Benelux'
'Maréchal Foch'	'La France'
'Deutschland'	'Goliath'

Practically all the early and mid-season pinks respond to this treatment. Where it is required to retain the pink colour, and have it intensified, it is recommended that phosphate should be included in the liquid feed in equal proportions with potash (see Appendix II).

Cytisus canariensis This beautiful plant, formerly known as *Genista canariensis*, was once regularly forced, but today is much less common, perhaps because it is rather difficult to propagate. Plants in flower are still sometimes sold in pots in March and April. The purchase of one of these is the best way of obtaining a stock. Small semi-ripe cuttings with a heel are taken in March or April, and are rooted in a propagator or a propagating case with bottom heat. Covering a pan full of such cuttings with polythene would be satisfactory, provided that bottom heat to about 21 °C (*70°F*) is available. The cuttings are difficult to establish after rooting, so as soon as they have produced roots they are transferred to small pots and placed back under the polythene until established.

They are best kept in a cold greenhouse or frame throughout their first summer and winter. As soon as the young shoot is growing it is stopped, and as the plant gets larger it is stopped again, with the object of building up a bushy head. In their second summer the plants stand outside on a standing-bed until the late autumn, when they are brought under glass for flowering the following spring. Thereafter they can be flowered every year, being put into progressively larger pots until they reach the 250 mm (*10 in*) size.

Forsythia intermedia and **Forsythia suspensa** Many deciduous spring and early-summer flowering shrubs can be cut when dormant, and brought into flower early in the spring to provide cut flowers for indoor decoration. Long straight branches are selected, and cut from January onwards. When placed in water in buckets at a temperature of 13–15°C (*55–60°F*) they soon come into flower.

Other shrubs that can be handled in the same way are *Deutzia gracilis* and *Prunus triloba*.

Chapter 25

Plant collections under glass

The alpine house

The name 'alpine house' may sound like a contradiction in terms; in fact it is a greenhouse used solely for housing collections of true hardy plants which need the protection it affords, not against low temperatures and frost, as is normally the case, but against rain and damp.

'True' alpine plants, which are adapted to withstand the rigours of altitude, such as wind, intense cold, snow cover and drought, find the mild damp conditions of an oceanic winter climate like that of the British Isles difficult to endure. The environment provided in the winter by an unheated well-ventilated greenhouse protects them from rain and damp, and makes it possible to grow spring-flowering plants of great beauty and charm. The alpine house suits not only this group of mountain and arctic plants, but a whole host of other attractive species including many small bulbs. The growing of plants in an alpine house has long been a form of gardening in its own right, offering many inducements, of which foremost are the absence of fuel costs, the vast range of subjects that can be grown and the ease of looking after them.

As the alpine house is required only to protect from rain and not to provide a warmer temperature, it follows that its ventilation must be adequate. Side ventilators inserted at the lowest level to increase the

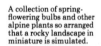
A collection of spring-flowering bulbs and other alpine plants so arranged that a rocky landscape in miniature is simulated.

'chimney effect' are essential if temperatures are to be kept as little above those of the outside air as is possible within a greenhouse. In fact, everything must be done to reduce the 'greenhouse effect' which sends temperatures rocketing up to unacceptable levels in sunny weather.

Alpines and their associates are always grown in containers, so the house requires staging on both sides in order that they can be placed at a level where they can easily be seen and enjoyed. Traditionally, the staging on which the containers (principally pots and pans) are placed has been covered with pea-gravel or grit. However, in the light of recent knowledge it is now clear that a 150 mm (6 in) deep layer of lime-free sand would be better and more effective in ensuring good drainage from the containers, which is absolutely essential in the case of alpines.

Enthusiasts like to grow their plants in clayware containers, mainly out of custom but also because the plants look better than they do in plastic ones, and clay pots do not become brittle with age like the plastic containers. However, alpines grow just as well in plastic pots.

Bearing in mind that alpines naturally grow best in such places as scree beds and rock fissures, it has been the practice to use gritty compost with rapid drainage properties and high air-filled porosity. Composts of the modern loamless type can have characteristics which suit the requirements of alpines: for example, sphagnum peat of the medium and coarser grades on its own has an air-filled porosity of 30–40 per cent. If it is mixed with 20 per cent by volume of coarse sand, i.e. greater than 3 mm (0.125 in) grist, the air-filled porosity will still be of the order of 30 per cent. This is probably higher than many traditional composts, and should be suitable for most alpines. The sand size is critical, as the smaller the grain-size below 3 mm grist, the more the sand will decrease the air-filled porosity of any of the materials with which it is mixed. Also, sands must be lime-free, because as little as 0.5 per cent of calcium carbonate (limestone) in the sand can raise the pH of a compost containing 25 per cent sand by as much as 0.7, which is another way of saying that it will make the compost five times more alkaline. As most alpines stay in their pots for a long time, there is a good case for growing them in a loam-based medium such as John Innes Potting Compost No. 1.

The nutritional needs of alpines are not considered to be very great; they are plants which have become adapted to grow in harsh environments of low fertility, and if given a rich diet, particularly of nitrogen-containing compounds, would grow in a manner which is lush and out of character. They would also become susceptible to various ills, fungal diseases in particular. There seems to be good evidence to support this view; but, on the other hand, the nutritional needs of alpines have not yet been scientifically investigated, and all that can be said with certainty is that if they are long-lived and spend a long time in the container, an occasional liquid feed is desirable, particularly if they show symptoms of nitrogen deficiency.

Reference has already been made to the fact that pans are greatly favoured for some alpines, particularly as they provide opportunities for miniature landscaping with small pieces of rock. The fact remains, however, that pans, being shallow, are not good containers, because the shallower the depth of compost in a container, the less well it drains; and consequently the less is its air-filled porosity. The deeper the container, the better, provided that it is standing on a medium with good drainage characteristics.

A miniature greenhouse designed to house alpine plants and small bulbs when they come into flower. The plants will be grown elsewhere — probably in a frame or service greenhouse — and then placed in the miniature display house when at their best.

A miniature greenhouse designed to house alpine plants and small bulbs when they come into flower. The plants will be grown elsewhere — probably in a frame or service greenhouse — and then placed in the miniature display house when at their best.

Another custom long-established in the growing of alpines in containers is that of covering the surface of the compost in the container with rock chippings. This is pleasing in appearance and sets off the plant very well. It is also good practice because it keeps their lower leaves, particularly those of rosette habit, away from the growing medium, and resting on a dry, airy surface. Its only disadvantage is that it makes it difficult to see or feel when the compost has become dry.

Most of the subjects grown are spring-flowering, and many of them are visually uninteresting when flowering is over. To deal with this situation it is convenient to run an alpine house in conjunction with a cold-frame to which plants can be moved until they are wanted again. Such a system has the added advantage that in summer the lights can be removed completely from the frame to leave all the plants fully exposed to summer weather. They can then be replaced again when damp weather returns in the autumn or if damp periods occur in the summer. It must be remembered that the lights are there only as a protection from damp, so they must always be 'chocked open' to provide ventilation. The house can be used in the summer for other purposes, but careful selection from the range of dwarf plants available will allow it to be of interest throughout most of the year. In fact, devising ways and means of doing this is part of the excitement and challenge of an alpine house.

The cool greenhouse

This is a term used to describe a greenhouse that is provided with a heating system which is set to prevent its temperature falling below 7°C (*45°F*). It rejoices under other names such as a half-hardy house, or temperate house, or even a Mediterranean house. Whatever its name, its essential feature is that it is frost-proof. The temperature of 7°C (*45°F*) was arrived at by trial and error in past decades, but accords well with more recent scientific measurements which define 6°C (*43°F*) as a cut-off point below which little or no plant growth takes place. In fact the suitability of a district for growing in the open certain crops such as sweet corn, tomatoes and vines is determined by measuring the accumulated degrees above a base of 6°C (*43°F*) that it enjoys. Accumulated degrees are calculated by summing time multiplied by temperature. The units are more commonly known as day-degrees. Tables similar to those used for calculating heating costs are available to show the relative earliness of different localities. A cool house could, in fact, be used to house all tender plants safely (even tropical ones, though they would virtually cease to grow during the winter), but its proper purpose is for housing collections of such plants as *Fuchsia, Pelargonium* (geranium), *Bougainvillaea, Hibiscus, Hoya, Stephanotis, Begonia* and the potted plants of commerce such as *Solanum, Cyclamen, Calceolaria,* bulbs like *Nerine, Amaryllis, Vallota,* the arum lilies and many of their numerous relatives, and (for those who like them) the grey-leaved plants of the Mediterranean.

It is difficult adequately to categorise the range of subjects, so this rough classification must suffice:

1. Woody evergreens, e.g. *Plumbago, Hoya, Hibiscus, Fuchsia, Jasminum, Solanum capsicastrum* and *S. jasminoides,* South African heaths, palms. They can be grown as pot plants, and the climbers (if space permits) can be planted in the soil and trained up wires or columns or, in the case of lean-to houses, against a wall. Although they are all perennials, a wise attitude is to regard them as having a short life and needing to be replaced fairly frequently by young specimens.

If grown as pot plants, they will require ever larger pots if they are to be kept in good condition, unless a programme of continual liquid feeding is adopted. With those which cannot tolerate alkaline conditions, and this is a very large number, care must be taken to ensure that the pH of the medium in which they are growing does not rise. This is an ever-present danger in hard-water areas, particularly with loamless composts.

2. Sub-shrubs, e.g. *Pelargonium,* marguerite, *Aphelandra, Artemisia,* some species of *Crassula,* some species of *Begonia,* etc.

These constitute a group of plants intermediate between woody perennials and perennial herbs. Many of them are of a succulent nature, and on balance respond to a dry regime. Many of them, if given a moist regime, produce lush growth which is out of character with their true appearance. Generalisations are difficult, and the gardener must devise his own management policy. Where there is a greenhouse border available, they can be planted out, and some (such as *Pelargonium*) can be trained against walls, but on the whole they have to be grown as potted plants. Like the woody perennials, they should be propagated fairly frequently, because they are more attractive as younger, smaller plants than as older, straggly ones.

3. Perennial herbs. These include an almost endless list of species, as much of the world's vegetation falls into this category. Some familiar examples are *Streptocarpus, Primula obconica, P. kewensis* and *P. malacoides*; several members of the family Gesneriaceae, including *Columnea, Saintpaulia*; many species of *Begonia* such as *B. rex* or *B. semperflorens, Peperomia, Bromelia, Maranta, Tradescantia, Zebrina.* Many are aquatic plants like *Cyperus*; and there are innumerable succulents, to say nothing of the orchids.

If the succulents, aquatics and epiphytic orchids are set to one side, most of the remainder can be grown in more or less the same way, which is in pots in standardised composts, and subjected to a continual liquid-feeding programme, Some have foibles, like *Saintpaulia*, where water must not be allowed to fall on its leaves; and some, such as the primulas, are slow-growing plants which do not require the same levels of feeding as more vigorous ones like *Coleus*.

4. Annual herbs and plants treated like annuals. These include the popular commercial flowering plants such as *Cinneraria, Calceolaria, Capsicum annuum, Thunbergia alatus* and autumn-sown half-hardy annuals dealt with elsewhere. Perennials, such as *Cyclamen persicum* and the primulas listed under perennial herbs, are usually raised from seed annually and treated as though they were annuals.

Seeds of these plants can be sown at almost any time of the year, but the normal practice for the flowering ones is to sow late in the summer or early in the autumn and to prick the seedlings out into trays or small pots, so that they are well established before the amount of light is too little for growth to take place. They do not require high temperatures, but when grown commercially are sometimes kept in heated frames. When growth picks up again in February they grow rapidly and flower in March and April.

Cyclamen takes much longer, and although many modern cultivars mature more rapidly, you should sow in September and expect the plants to flower one year later. This is a plant that does not respond to high temperatures and requires to be kept cool in the summer by means of shading, as ventilation will never cool the environment sufficiently.

The summer-flowering annuals like *Thunbergia* are sown in the spring, as is *Capsicum annuum* (Pepper) grown for its coloured fruits in autumn and winter.

5. Herbaceous perennials. Most of the tender herbaceous plants die down to survive the drought of the dry season, not the low temperatures of winter. Some of them are bulbs, of which the most notable are *Nerine, Amaryllis, Clivea, Hippeastrum, Vallota* and *Veltheimia*, all belonging to the amaryllis family, Amaryllidaceae, except the last, which belongs to the lily family, Liliaceae. Others which have a dormant period in which the foliage dies down are the various arum lilies, which when started into growth require marsh conditions.

The bulbs mentioned, which largely originate in South Africa, can be grown in greenhouse borders but are more commonly grown in pots. The hippeastrums are particularly showy, and a wide range of cultivars is available. They, and similar large bulbs, are planted in large pots, 200 mm (*8 in*) being about the smallest size that will accommodate them. A compost with the nutrient content of John Innes No. 3 is best. After they have been potted, the compost is watered, but no further watering is attempted until growth has started. Thereafter they are watered on a continual liquid-feeding basis until flowering is over and the leaves are showing signs of dying back. Water is then increasingly withheld until the bulb has become dormant or nearly so (some species – *Clivea*, for example – maintain leaves throughout and are not, therefore, truly herbaceous). During the period of dormancy which gardeners call the 'resting period', warmth is considered essential to simulate the dry season of their natural habitat and to encourage the developmental processes occurring within

A *Hippeastrum* (a tender bulb) in flower in the spring. After flowering and a certain amount of leaf growth the plant will become dormant, during which period it should be kept warm and dry to simulate the dry season of its native South Africa.

the bulbs. After dormancy the whole cycle is repeated. With some bulbs, growth starts in the autumn and dormancy starts in early summer, but others grow in the spring and lie dormant much later.

6. Special collections. *(a) Cacti and succulents* – The cultivation of these spectacular and often bizarre plants has a great following, and many specialist books are available. Cacti is horticultural jargon for members of the family Cactaceae of which there are about 1,500 species arranged within 25 genera. Similar to them in appearance, although botanically quite different, are the South African xerophytic species of *Euphorbia* (the spurges). The succulents are mostly members of the family Crassulaceae, and – though xerophytes (i.e. adapted to grow in arid situations) like the Cactaceae and *Euphorbia* – they differ from them in not having thorns or prickles. *Crassula, Sedum, Sempervivum, Kalenchöe* and *Briophyllum* are the best known genera; *Agave* and *Aloe* are succulents quite unrelated to the crassulas, but similarly adapted to withstand drought.

A collection of cacti and
succulents grown in
containers and staged on a
greenhouse bench.

Being mostly desert plants they quite clearly lend themselves to growing
in a greenhouse where dry conditions are maintained, and although
heating is required to bring this about in the winter, it is not generally
needed in the summer. They can be planted in a greenhouse border, whose
surface should be covered (mulched) with rock chippings for the same
reasons as given for alpines. In pots, a compost with a high proportion of
air-filled pores is essential.

The nutritional needs of this group of plants have not been scientifically
established, but it is assumed that, as they are slow-growing, they do not
require very much. However, an occasional liquid feed in the summer is no
bad thing. In summer they are watered more frequently than in the winter,
when they hardly need watering at all. It is impossible to specify how often
a cactus in a pot should be watered in the summer time, because so much
depends on the size of the plant and that of the container in which it is
growing. Experienced cactus growers give the advice 'when in doubt, do
not water'. A rule-of-thumb method is to water a pot once to every two
times a normal plant in the same sized pot is watered in the summer time,
and once to every three times in the winter. A well-ventilated house should
not need shading in the summer.

(b) Orchids – With 15,000 species, and half that number in cultivation or
worthy of it, the orchid enthusiast (or orchidist, as he likes to be known) is
not likely to run out of interest. Orchids are divisible, on the basis of their
habitats, into epiphytic and terrestrial orchids. Among experts the
former are often called orchids and the latter orchis.

Epiphytic orchids are essentially plants of the rain forests. They are
found growing on trees in crotches, in forks or in any niche where moss and
debris can accumulate and be moistened by rain and drips. In cultivation
this habitat is simulated by packing them in pots in a mixture of

A fine specimen of an orchid of the genus *Cymbidium* in flower in a pot. This is a popular orchid: one of the easiest to grow and one of the most showy. It is extensively used for cut blooms.

sphagnum moss and osmunda fern fibre. If the latter is unobtainable, sphagnum, on its own, may have to suffice. *Cymbidium*, which is one of the best known and most widely grown orchids, can be grown satisfactorily in coarse sphagnum-moss peat.

The roots of epiphytic orchids, and probably of all orchids, live in association with various species of fungus, known collectively as mycorrhiza, which assist the plant in its nutrition. The mechanism is complicated and not fully understood, but overall the fungus acts as an intermediary making the nutrients in the decaying organic debris available to the orchid, which in its turn provides the fungus with the carbohydrates it has manufactured by photosynthesis.

Many of the epiphytic orchids, to give of their best, require higher temperatures than are provided by the cool house and thus can be an expensive form of gardening, but some, notably the cymbidiums, can be managed in temperate conditions.

The terrestrial orchids (grown in the soil) are nearly all plants of the temperate zones of the northern hemisphere. They can, if hardy, be grown in frames and put into the alpine house (or any other cool house) to flower, but if they are tender the cool-house environment is more suitable.

As the epiphytic orchids are very exacting in their requirements, it was the practice in the days of large private gardens to set aside a greenhouse specifically for them. As so few can now afford such luxuries, however, the subject of growing them warrants only scant treatment here. Those stimulated to become orchidists are referred to the very extensive literature on the subject.

A tropical house is one for growing tropical plants. Victorians referred to it as the 'stove', and it has also been called the 'warm-temperate house'. Equatorial temperatures hover around 32°C *(90°F)*, but can go much

The tropical house

higher in the middle of the day – though not in tropical rain forests where the cloud cover has a stabilising effect. To think of setting a greenhouse thermostat at 32°C (*90°F*) is really quite fanciful, but to maintain tropical vegetation in good condition the minimum temperature tolerable will have to be about 13°C (*55°F*). Providing for this against normal contingencies means a heating system capable of a temperature lift of 20 C° (*36 F°*) which is an expensive undertaking (see Chapter 5 and Appendix I).

If the expenditure involved is considered possible, the problem is still not quite solved because the size of the house is a limiting factor to the range of plants that can be considered. Tropical vegetation tends to be both vigorous and large, and a few small plants can soon grow to fill what once seemed a large space. This limitation restricts the choice of species to the perennial herbs and smaller woody plants, such as *Codaeum* (croton), the bromeliads which include the pineapple, the epiphytic orchids and a host of plants with attractive foliage too numerous to mention. Tropical palms can be accommodated only while they remain small. Keeping small is really the keynote of an interesting tropical collection, because as these plants become large they acquire a somewhat monotonous appearance. Those who have seen tropical vegetation in the wild often comment on its variety of forms but also on the monotony of its greenness.

Keeping small really means frequent propagation. Although plants can be kept small by restricting their roots within the confines of small pots, the resulting starvation produces hard, faded-looking specimens with no appeal at all, but as soon as they are fed they romp away to the point where

A simulated tropical landscape within a greenhouse. A tropical pool is edged with papyrus and has various climbing plants and other tropical rain-forest vegetation surrounding it.

they are too big for the pot. This is when they should be replaced by young successors. Tropical collections, large or small, require moist régimes, so a highly automated watering system is desirable (see Chapter 9).

A house plant can only mean a plant taken into a dwelling-house for some period of time. The term was first used to identify subjects which because of their shade-tolerance could survive for a long time in the environment of a room where all the natural light available came through a window. In Victorian times the plants in fashion were the aspidistra, the so-called asparagus ferns, *Asparagus plumosus* and *A. sprengeri*, the real ferns *Nephrolepis* and *Adiantum* (Maidenhair fern), and the juvenile form of the Norfolk Island Pine *Araucaria excelsa*. By 1939 the fashion had gone completely, but was revived in the 1950s with an entirely new cast.

House plants

This time it was cultivars of the ivies (*Hedera*), the southern-hemisphere vines (*Cissus antarctica* and *Rhoicissus rhomboideae*), *Ficus elastica*, known as the Rubber Plant, and the relatives of the arum lily (aroids) such as *Monstera, Philodendron* and *Scindapsus*. This market was so successful that the production of these foliage plants increased almost exponentially, with the world's tropical and sub-tropical flora being searched for new or little-known species that would lend themselves to the purpose. Beautifully illustrated guides to the care and recognition of house plants have been published, and to these the reader is referred.

Probably the most enduring house plants are those woody perennials which are members of the ivy family, Araliaceae. They include *Hedera* (the ivies), of which there is a wide range of cultivars, *Fatsia japonica*, × *Fatshedera* (a hybrid between *Fatsia* and *Hedera*) and the dainty-leaved *Dizygotheca elegantissima*. Their success is due to the fact that they are temperate-zone plants, shade-tolerant; and, while they are not xerophytes, they are tolerant of a dry, as distinct from an arid, régime. The vines *Rhoicissus* and *Cissus*, though in no way related to the Araliaceae, can be placed in the same category, as can the various species of *Ficus*, all cousins of the fig, although they respond to somewhat warmer conditions and are best in centrally-heated homes.

The evergreen aroids, such as species of *Dieffenbachia, Monstera, Philodendron, Scindapsus, Anthurium*; the family Marantaceae which includes *Maranta, Calathea* and *Ctenanthe*; the peperomias, the begonias; and, in the family Commelinaceae, the trailing tradescantias, zebrinas and setcreasias – all these make up a hard core of perennial herbs, capable of long stays in centrally-heated dwellings.

The one quality all house plants must have in common is shade-tolerance, because the brightest room in the brightest house in summer is a pretty dark place when compared with the daylight outdoors.

With a greenhouse, you are in the fortunate position of being able to provide your long-stay house plants with an annual period of rehabilitation.

Lists of house plants always include plants normally grown for the beauty of their flowers. Such plants must generally be grown in a greenhouse until they are in flower, before they are brought into the home.

Techniques of cultivation

Raising plants under glass

One of the most useful contributions a greenhouse makes to gardening is the facility it provides for raising vegetables and flowers from seed, in order to get them off to a good start in the interests of earliness, high yield and the avoidance of certain pest and disease problems.

Looking at vegetables and salad plants first, there follows a section on each one which can, with advantage, be raised under glass.

Garden peas

Peas are welcome vegetables. The earlier they can be obtained, the better they seem to be, and the less they suffer from the pea moth and mildew. Sown early in the garden, germination is often disappointing, as the hazards from slugs, and from the soil-borne fungi which cause pre-emergence rots, are considerable. Sowing three or four seeds in 63 mm ($2\frac{1}{2}$ in) pots produces little clumps of peas which can be planted out when they are about 37 mm ($1\frac{1}{2}$ in) high, 150–225 mm (6–9 in) apart in a row. These will give excellent results. An unheated greenhouse is all that is required. Sowings can be made in February with seeds which have been treated with a fungicidal dressing.

Garden peas raised in small pots for planting out in the garden. The two pots in the foreground show a batch of peas just germinating, whereas the two in the background are ready for hardening-off and planting out.

Broad beans

Autumn sowings of broad beans have to be made with varieties not considered to be of the best quality, but they do have the great advantage that they produce plants that are not attacked by black bean aphids. Similar advantages can be obtained by sowing more popular varieties in February singly in pots and planting out in March or April. Heat is not required.

Broad beans germinated in
75mm (*3in*) pots under
glass, and now ready for
hardening-off and planting
out in the garden.

Dwarf French and runner beans

These are half-hardy plants and cannot be planted out until all danger of frost has passed, which is usually towards the end of May. Germination is often spasmodic, hence the traditional practice of sowing two beans per station, removing one if both germinate. Sowing singly in 75 mm (*3 in*) pots or 43 mm (*1¾ in*) peat blocks in mid- to late April makes it possible to have complete rows of early heavy-yielding plants. In soils where disappointment in the germination of runner beans is often experienced, there is much to be said for sowing even main crops in containers. To germinate successfully, they need a soil temperature of at least 15°C (*60°F*).

Lettuces

Lettuces can be sown outdoors in March when the weather and the nature of the soil permit the preparation of a seedbed. They then take from 12 to 14 weeks to produce hearted plants, which is towards the end of June. Earlier supplies can be obtained from young plants grown in pots or 27 mm (*1.1 in*) peat blocks, planted out successively from mid-March onwards. Lettuces are required in such small quantities that, for the average family, batches of no more than six plants planted out at fortnightly intervals provide at least as much as will be consumed. This is a case where pelleted seed comes into its own. The pellets are sown singly into pots or 27 mm (*1.1 in*) peat blocks, preferably the latter: the first sowing is in late September, and the plants are overwintered under glass and planted out in mid-March; the second is in February for planting at the end of March; an early March sowing gives plants for planting in mid-April, and so on. Once May has come, the seed germinates better if the containers are kept outdoors in an uncovered frame. The butterhead varieties of lettuce do not germinate satisfactorily at temperatures above 25°C (*77°F*), and must be kept cool by watering and shading. There is some evidence to suggest that cheaper production is possible if three seeds are placed in one pot or block. When planted out the three plants develop quite satisfactorily provided they have a circle of about 500 mm (*20 in*) diameter in which to grow. The total abandonment of open-ground sowing has many attractions.

Lettuce plants raised in peat blocks from pelleted seed, now ready for hardening-off and planting in the garden. If some of these are planted under low polythene tunnels, and some in the open ground, a succession is obtained.

Onions

In the production of bulb onions, as opposed to salad onions, large bulbs can be obtained only by giving the longest season of growth possible before bulbing starts, which happens when the day becomes longer than about sixteen hours. An early start by germinating under glass, therefore, is a recognised method of getting onions of good size. Onions germinate at temperatures above 7°C (*45°F*), so if they can be given temperatures of about 15°C (*60°F*), excellent germination should ensue. It is usual to sow onions in a seed tray, but an alternative is to sow six or nine seeds per pot or block. If heat is available, the seed is sown in January and the blocks of seedlings are planted out, after hardening-off in frames, in March. The recommended density of planting for transplanted onions is 65–85 per square metre (*6–8 per square foot*), which is achieved by spacing them 50

A box of multi-seeded onions in peat blocks at the stage where they are ready for planting in the soil. Each block contains on average five onion plants. These will be planted in the garden 300mm (*12in*) apart in both directions, and grow as a bunch.

mm (*2 in*) apart in rows 300 mm (*12 in*) apart. When planting out blocks containing six seedlings, they should be 300 mm (*12 in*) apart in rows 300 mm (*12 in*) apart to achieve the same density. If very large onions are wanted three seeds only are sown per block and the distance adjusted proportionally. Large onions, however, are not wanted by everybody. The same procedure can be used for the August-sown Japanese varieties.

Leeks

These are not planted out until quite late, in May or June, because they take a long time from sowing until they are large enough to transplant. They are often sown by amateurs in February in seed trays, and placed in cold-frames or unheated greenhouses. An alternative is to grow four seedlings per 27 mm (*1.1 in*) block. These would be planted out in May. The normal density for leeks is 22 per square metre (*2 per square foot*). If planting clumps of three or four, the distance between them should be 300 mm (*12 in*) in the row and 450 mm (*18 in*) between each row.

The cabbage family

All the plants commonly called brassicas by gardeners are cultivars of the wild cabbage *Brassica oleracea*. They include all the various cabbages, Brussels sprouts, cauliflowers, broccoli, kales and kohlrabi – an extraordinary assortment. The seeds of all these types germinate readily

Young Brussels sprouts seedlings grown in peat blocks. Two or three seeds were sown in each block and covered with sand, and after germination reduced to one seedling per block. The six blocks on the left have not yet been thinned, whereas the six on the right were thinned two or three weeks ago.

within a wide range of temperatures, 5°C to 32°C (*41–90°F*), so the purpose of sowing them under glass is not to get better germination, but merely to regulate the supply and to avoid the transplanting check. For example, a pinch of Brussels sprout seed sown in a 75 mm (*3 in*) pot will provide all the plants that a garden is likely to need. If the seedlings are transferred one to each 75 mm (*3 in*) pot and hardened-off as soon as established in it, they will be ready for planting in the garden two or three weeks later, where they will develop with hardly any check whatsoever. Even that excellent summer sprouting broccoli called 'calabrese', which does so well from direct sowing, is worth starting in pots or peat blocks if F1 varieties are being used, because the seed is very expensive and there is very little in a packet.

One of the best of the brassicas is the early-summer cauliflower, which should be sown under unheated glass in the third week of September. As soon as the seedlings have emerged they are pricked off into 87 mm ($3\frac{1}{2}$ in) pots, overwintered in the greenhouse, and planted out in the garden from mid-February until late March depending on soil and climate. Plants put out early sometimes develop a malformation described as whiptail. This is due to a deficiency of the element molybdenum within the plant. Watering the pots before planting out with a solution of sodium molybdate at 6 grams per litre (1 oz per gallon) usually prevents the trouble.

Summer cabbages of the drumhead type such as 'Primo' or 'Golden Acre' are sown in unheated houses in early February and pricked-off for planting out in April. In no circumstances should they be given high temperatures. Non-bolting strains of seed should be sought. They must not be planted out in very cold weather as low temperatures induce bolting. Seeds of brassicas, if stored properly, are very long lived, up to nine years; so the technique of sowing a pinch of seed in a small flower pot means that a packet will last a long time – a thought not likely to endear itself to the seedsmen!

Celery

Both the self-blanching summer celery as well as the trench or winter celery must be raised under glass, because the seed will not germinate until the temperature of the soil has reached 10°C (50°F). This does not happen until May, which would not leave sufficient growing season. Celery seed, therefore, is best germinated at about 15°C (60°F) in a heated greenhouse in early March. The seed is sown in trays or in a small pot depending upon the number of seedlings wanted. The seedlings do very well if they can be pricked-off into peat blocks of the 80 × 80 mm size ($3\frac{1}{4}$ × $3\frac{1}{4}$ in). By the end of March they can move to a cold-frame for hardening-off. They must not be planted out until the soil temperature is well above 5°C (42°F), or else bolting will occur. Pelleted seed for single-seed sowing is now available to commercial growers and may soon be for the amateur.

Marrows, courgettes and cucumbers

The propagation of greenhouse or English cucumbers has already been described (see Chapter 15), but here we are referring to the modern F1 hybrid ridge cucumbers such as 'Sutton's Burpless Tasty Green', which are of a quality almost comparable with greenhouse ones. These, together with marrows and courgettes, require a temperature of at least 15°C (60°F) in order to germinate successfully. In all cases the seed is sown singly as described for greenhouse cucumbers. It is not safe to plant them out until June other than in the warmest parts of Britain.

Sweet corn

This requires the same treatment, insofar as temperature is concerned, as cucumbers and marrows, and should not be planted out until the temperature of the soil is approaching 15°C (60°F). Sowing the seeds singly in 80 mm × 80 mm ($3\frac{1}{4}$ × $3\frac{1}{4}$ in) peat blocks is probably the best method.

Tomatoes

Outdoor tomatoes should be raised with the same care and precision as indoor ones, but as they cannot be planted out until the end of May or the beginning of June, sowing needs to be six weeks earlier, in mid-April.

Potatoes

Scientific investigation into the cultivation of the potato has been considerable in recent years: far too much to reproduce here. In brief, early potatoes should be sprouted ('chitted') under glass, starting in September or October, by placing them in trays with the rose end (the end with all the eyes) uppermost in a temperature of 18°C (*65°F*). When the eyes are well and truly breaking into growth, the temperature is lowered to 7°C (*45°F*), at which it remains until nearer planting time, when it can rise again. This treatment should result in a small number of sprouts, ideally about two only. Maincrop seed potatoes are put in trays in the same way, but are kept at the lower temperature of 7°C (*45°F*) until just before planting time; this should result in a larger number of sprouts. *

*A useful book to consult is P. J. Salter, J. K. A. Bleasedale *et al., Know and Grow Vegetables* (Oxford University Press, 1979 (Part 1), 1982 (Part 2)).

Flowers

Flowering plants raised from seed under glass are generally referred to as summer bedding plants, even if they are not actually intended for this purpose. Millions of annual bedding plants, both hardy and half-hardy, are raised every year by nurserymen for the retail trade and sold in a variety of ways: until the age of thermoplastics, peat and soil blocks, and biodegradable containers, the standard wooden seed tray was universally used. Today, many ingenious devices, in which plants are grown in separate compartments in single packs, are used for easier marketing as well as to reduce the transplanting check which normally besets bedding plants after they have been planted out. Ingenious and convenient though these containers are, you can produce better plants by using blocks or biodegradable containers and slow-release fertilisers.

Before, however, embarking on any plan to raise bedding plants from seed you should satisfy yourself that the exercise is worthwhile, because all hardy annuals and most half-hardy annuals can be sown in the garden to produce beautiful riots of colours, in a random and informal pattern. Such sowings are made either broadcast or in short rows, and are then thinned to the desired density. Plants raised under glass are strictly for formal displays, usually designed in strict geometrical patterns, and with the advantage that the display can come about earlier in the season.

Without doubt the peat block is the best unit in which to raise the more showy bedding plants, among which are included:

1. *Antirrhinum major* – Snapdragon
2. *Begonia* –fibrous-rooted bedding cultivars
3. *Callistephus sinensis* – China Aster
4. *Celosia cristata* – Cockscomb
5. *Celosia cristata* 'Pyrimidalis' – Plumed Cockscomb
6. *Cleome spinosa* – Spider Flower
7. *Impatiens holstii* and *I. sultani* – Busy Lizzy
8. *Kochia scoparia* 'Tricophylla' – Burning Bush
9. *Penstemon* hybrids
10. *Petunia* (hybrids of *Petunia integrifolia* and *P. myctaginiflora*)
11. *Rudbeckia* 'Sutton's Marmalade' and 'Rustic Dwarfs'
12. *Salvia splendens* (many cultivars) – Bedding Salvia
13. *Tagetes erecta* – African Marigold
14. *Tagetes patula* – French Marigold
15. *Zinnia elegans*

If the seed is large, or pelleted, it can be sown individually into the container, otherwise it must be in a pot or tray and pricked-off as soon as it can be handled. With summer bedding plants, heat is an advantage in all cases, and with the more tender half-hardy kinds it is a necessity. Germination is most rapid at a temperature of 18°C (*65°F*), although at 15°C (*60°F*) it will be satisfactory.

Other annuals, such as *Lobelia erinus* (forms of this are the blue garden Lobelias), *Lobularia maritima* (Sweet Alyssum) and *Ageratum houstonianum* (Blue Ageratum), which are so valuable for edging, can be grown individually with advantage. However, if space is at a premium, pricking-off into trays gives excellent plants provided that spacing is generous. The nurseryman's spacing of fifty-four plants per tray gives each plant 14.5 cm² (2¼ *sq in*) in which to grow, which is by no means generous. In the 63 mm (2½ *in*) deep nursery tray each plant would have only about 90 cm³ (5.5 *in³*) in which to develop. Compare this with 512 cm³ (31 *in³*) in an 80 mm (3¼ *in*) cubic peat block. All this points to the fact that to grow good sized plants in trays, they need to be at least 63 mm (2½ *in*) apart in each direction in the same depth of soil. This will provide 257 cm³ (15.7 *in³*) of soil for the roots of each plant to colonise, which is still only about half that provided by the 80 mm (3¼ *in*) blocks. This explains the overwhelming popularity of blocks on the part of commercial growers.

The time for sowing annuals depends to some extent on how much heat can be afforded. Early to mid-March is a good time to start, because it means pricking-off will be done early in April, which will produce plants ready for hardening-off in cold-frames from late April through May, for planting out in early June. This can be varied according to the local climate, and to whether the plants are intended to follow spring bedding plants or not. Most hardy annuals grow satisfactorily at temperatures between 10°C and 15°C (50–60°F), whereas the tender half-hardy annuals need soil and air temperatures above 15°C (60°F), and a few of the very tender plants will need even higher temperatures.

A fine batch of seedlings growing in a compartmentalised plastic tray which fits within a stronger tray. These plants, when hardened-off, can be planted out into the flower garden without receiving any transplanting check. They may benefit from liquid feeding at a slightly later stage, unless slow-release fertiliser was included in the compost mix in which they are growing.

Chapter 27

Propagation

tomatoes, cucumbers, melons, peppers and aubergines

Tomatoes The earlier a crop of tomatoes is required to be, the more critical its propagation becomes. Conversely, the later the crop, the less demanding the process, although care is still needed. Propagation is here described fairly fully so that you can decide what is most appropriate to your own circumstances.

In order to provide the earliest crops tomato plants are set out in their growing stations in January and February. In northern England planting in January is not considered worthwhile because light intensities are not sufficiently high. To get plants as early as this sowings are made in mid-November in southern England, and early December in the north. For planting in early March, sowing is delayed until the end of December or beginning of January. Early February sowings produce plants for late March and early April plantings, a period most likely to interest the amateur with a heated greenhouse. Finally, plants for cold houses are sown in early March in the south of England and mid-March in the north.

Whatever the sowing date, the requirements for sowing the seeds are the same. First of all there is a general preference for sowing the seed in loamless seed composts such as the GCRI seed compost already described. The seeds are sown thinly, giving each seed 4–5 cm^2 (*about 1 sq in*) in which to grow. Whatever the compost, it is placed in the container, thoroughly soaked and then left for some hours to drain. Containers may be trays, pots or pans according to the number of plants required, but whatever is used a depth of compost greater than 60 mm ($2\frac{1}{2}$ *in*) is not required. The surface of the compost should be slightly firmed and, of course, level. The seed is covered lightly with compost, about 3 mm ($\frac{1}{8}$ *in*) being sufficient, and this is moistened carefully with a fine spray. To prevent the surface of the compost drying the container is covered with a sheet of glass or milky polythene. If glass is used at a time when sunshine is likely, it must be shaded to prevent the small volume of air trapped between the glass and the compost becoming too hot, which it rapidly will. As soon as germination occurs the covering is promptly removed.

After germination, and as soon as the seed leaves (or cotyledons) have expanded, the seedlings are transferred to pots, where once again a peat-based potting compost is preferred. A considerable amount of research has gone into establishing the best size of pot for raising tomatoes, and it is now agreed that a 110 mm ($4\frac{1}{4}$ *in*) diameter pot gives the best plant. In certain circumstances the growers of very early crops even use 125 mm (*5 in*) pots, but this is unlikely for the amateur. Rigid plastic pots are usual, but there are acceptable alternatives such as the so-called 'whalehide' pots and other biodegradable containers which are not removed at planting time. Peat blocks are also extensively used, but need to be 80 mm ($3\frac{1}{4}$ *in*) square and of similar depth.

The pots are filled with moist compost, very lightly tapped, and then the surplus compost is struck off level with the rim of the pot. A hole is made in the compost with a dibber and the tiny seedling is pricked-off carefully and the compost nestled around it. The pot is then watered, which settles the unfirmed compost down, leaving sufficient space at the top of the pot to provide what gardeners call 'watering space'.

As the young plants grow they have to be spaced out, so that they always stand clear of each other. If for reasons of space they ever have to be placed on the greenhouse floor, they should be on strips of polythene to prevent the roots entering the soil thus risking both contamination from soil-borne diseases and the check which results when these roots are broken. The young plants soon use up the nutrient reserves of the compost, and liquid feeding commences when the fifth rough leaf has expanded. The stock solution for the feed is made by dissolving 150 grams of potassium nitrate in one litre of water (*3 oz per pint*) and diluting it to 1 in 200 (one 5 ml spoonful per litre; *0.8 fl oz per gallon*). When a proprietory loamless compost is being used, the manufacturer's instructions should be studied carefully because the nutrients provided as fertiliser additives may be incomplete, so that other nutrients are required in addition to the potassium and nitrogen contained in the standard feed just described. As the plants increase in size, and particularly when brighter weather comes, watering will be necessary once a day and sometimes perhaps twice a day.

It may be of interest to the amateur to know of some of the special measures taken by professional growers. To compensate for the low light intensities of mid-winter, fluorescent lighting tubes are mounted over the young plants in specially designed growing rooms from which natural light is excluded. The tubes are about 150 mm (*6 in*) apart and about 900 mm (*3 ft*) above the plants so that they receive a light intensity of 15,000 lux. Tomatoes must have about eight hours of darkness per 24 hours, so for reasons of economy the bank of lights is usually constructed so that it can illuminate one batch of plants for twelve hours and an adjoining batch for the next twelve. Throughout, the temperature is maintained at 21 °C (*70°F*).

An alternative to this highly sophisticated method is to supplement natural daylight in the greenhouse by suspending high-pressure mercury vapour lamps or high-pressure sodium lamps over a batch of tomato seedlings to give a light intensity of 8,000–11,000 lux. This supplementary lighting is given for sixteen hours, including the hours of daylight, so that the plants still have their eight hours of darkness. Whichever method is used, the period from sowing to planting can be reduced by about four weeks, and often a better plant is produced.

The other aid to sophisticated growing is that of carbon dioxide (CO_2) enrichment of the atmosphere. The rate of enrichment is about threefold, i.e. the normal atmospheric content of CO_2, which is 300 parts per million, is raised to 900 or 1000 ppm. The normal method of producing the gas is by burning propane in special burners within the greenhouse. These are usually linked to a photo-electric cell which shuts the burners off at dusk and brings them on at dawn. They are also linked to the ventilators and to wind-speed sensors so that the burners are automatically shut off when the vents are open or the house is too draughty, so that wastage of this expensive gas is reduced.

Great attention has been given to the temperatures at which tomatoes are propagated and those at which they are subsequently grown. Recommended temperatures are published in Great Britain by the Ministry of

Agriculture, Fisheries and Food. Germination should be at a constant temperature of 20°C (*68°F*) with the ventilators set to open at 24°C (*75°F*). From the time of pricking-out until the first truss is just visible at the top of the plant the daytime temperature of 20°C (*68°F*) is still maintained, but the night temperature is allowed to drop to 15°C (*60°F*). From the time the truss is visible until the first flower opens, which is when the plant is ready to go into its growing station, the daytime temperature is kept at 18°C (*64°F*) until the end of February, and after that is allowed to rise again to 20°C (*68°F*). During the same period the night temperature is still allowed to drop back to 15°C (*60°F*). The ventilators throughout are set to open at 24°C (*75°F*).

The amateur might well be downcast by this account of the precise measures used to produce tomato plants, but he can take some comfort from the fact that a less precise regime will still give him tomato plants which are quite acceptable, although their performance will be reduced. He can also take comfort from the fact that plants sown from the middle of February to the middle of March are very much easier to raise, because light intensities are increasing all the time. Even if he cannot give his plants supplementary lighting and CO_2 enrichment he should do his best with the temperatures and stick rigidly to the recommended pot sizes and liquid feeding.

Cucumbers

Cucumbers are sown from November through until March and even later, according to the desired planting date. John Innes compost is quite suitable but in recent years a general preference for a peat compost such as GCRI has come about.

The seeds are sown singly in 62 mm ($2\frac{1}{2}$ *in*) pots which are well watered and covered with glass or milky polythene. There has been considerable discussion as to whether or not the seed should be put into the compost point down, laid flat or edge down. The last of these has now been agreed to be the most likely to aid rapid emergence of the seed leaves after germination.

As soon as the roots have developed in the pots, but before they emerge from the holes at the bottom, the plants are transferred to 125 mm (*5 in*) pots in which, supported by a 450 mm (*18 in*) cane, they grow until ready for planting out. In no circumstances should potting be firm: all that is necessary is to tap the pot and leave subsequent watering to bring about the required consolidation.

As the young plants develop they must be 'roomed out' so that no mutual shading occurs. Liquid feeding does not become necessary until the roots have colonised the compost in the larger pots, by which time they should be 225–300 mm high (*9–12 in*). The nutrient needs of the cucumber differ markedly from those of the tomato and their requirement seems only to be for nitrogen. Accordingly the liquid-feed stock solution is made by dissolving 150 grams of ammonium nitrate in 1 litre of water (*1$\frac{1}{2}$ lb per gallon*) and diluting this at the standard rate of 1 in 200 (one 5ml spoonful per litre; *0.8 fl oz per gallon*) to make the liquid feed. They are watered with this until ready for planting, which is when they are 375–450 mm high (*15–18 in*). Under optimum conditions this takes about seven weeks for an early sowing and five weeks for later ones.

The temperature requirements are as exacting for cucumbers as they are for tomatoes: to germinate the seeds 27°C (*80°F*) is needed to ensure rapid emergence (essential for modern F1 cultivars); once above the

Three cucumber seeds placed in a pot. The one on the left lies flat, the one in the centre is on its edge, and the one on the right is inserted point downwards. Tests have shown that placing the seed on its edge provides a slight advantage over the other methods, although in all cases the seed would germinate. Only one seed, of course, would be sown per container.

surface best results come from a night temperature of 18°C (*66°F*) and a daytime one of 21°C (*70°F*). The ventilators should be opened if the day temperature rises above 27°C (*80°F*). The amateur will find this régime difficult to achieve, but he must remember that any falling away from it will seriously delay the rate of development of very early sowings. Very early sowing is thus a doubtful proposition. If you are content with sowing in March when light intensities are much higher you will find the whole procedure much more straightforward.

Professional growers use supplementary lighting in exactly the same way as tomato growers, with the same improvement in the quality of the plant, subsequent increase in early yield and foreshortening of the propagation period. One interesting difference between the cucumber and the tomato is that the former can receive artificial illumination for the whole 24 hours per day without any ill effect.

Melons

Melons are sown in exactly the same way as cucumbers in a peat compost in 62 mm (*2½ in*) pots. The germination temperature is normally given as 21°C (*70°F*) but probably 27°C (*80°F*) is better. Early crops should be potted on with 125 mm (*5 in*) pots in the same way and at the same time as cucumbers. With later crops of melons, particularly the cantaloups, this is not necessary, and they can go into their permanent positions from the 62 mm (*2½ in*) pots.

Sweet peppers

The propagation of this plant closely resembles that of tomatoes, except that it takes somewhat longer to reach the planting-out stage. Sowing for the earliest crops takes place in mid-November in southern England to provide plants for planting out in mid-February. In northern England, sowing in mid-December is the earliest that can be contemplated and this gives plants for early-March planting. January and February sowings are ready for planting from mid-March to early April, and March sowings yield plants for cold houses and polythene tunnels in which they are planted in the middle of May.

The germination temperature is the same as for tomatoes and the seedlings should be pricked-off into 62 mm (*2½ in*) pots as soon as large enough to handle. They remain in these pots until the roots have ramified through the compost, which takes some four weeks for early sowings but less for later ones. They are then transferred to 110 mm (*4¼ in*) pots using the same potting technique as described for tomatoes. Towards the latter part of their stay in these pots liquid feeding as for tomatoes is required. The recommended temperature régime for the plants in pots is once again identical to that for tomatoes.

Aubergines

Aubergines are similar to the other plants in this chapter, except that it is unusual to strive for earliness; a sowing made in early March should produce plants early enough for most purposes. Delaying until the end of March will reduce the heat requirement and produce plants that will satisfy most people's needs.

Chapter 28

Forced crops

There is no agreement on the precise meaning of the term 'forced crop'. It could be argued that any plant grown under glass for the purpose of making it crop earlier and perhaps more heavily is forced. Here, however, the term is used in the restricted sense of plants which are grown in the open, then lifted when dormant, brought into a heated greenhouse and forced into early growth. Four plants are treated in this way: rhubarb, chicory, seakale, and asparagus.

Rhubarb

The dormant root stock of rhubarb is known as a crown. Two-year-old crowns are used for forcing. These are raised by dividing a two-year-old (or more) rhubarb crown into 'sets'. The old crowns are lifted as soon as they become dormant, and are cut with a half-moon lawn-edging tool into four or five pieces. It is usual, when dividing the crown, to cut through large buds, as this causes surrounding small buds to develop and yield, in due course, a larger crown than would have otherwise been the case. The sets are planted 750 mm (*2 ft 6 in*) apart in a row, so that the top of the set is just covered. In the spring, when growth starts, the set sometimes shrinks and ceases to be in close contact with the soil. If this happens it must be trodden firm or it might die. The land is dressed before planting with a compound fertiliser (18 per cent nitrogen/10–12 per cent phosphate/10–12 per cent potash) at a rate of 120 grams per square metre (*4 oz per sq yd*). During the two summers which follow, a nitrogen fertiliser is applied as a top dressing to encourage the growth of the crown. Ammonium nitrate at 30 grams per square metre (*1 oz per sq yd*), or ammonium sulphate or Nitro-Chalk at 50 grams per square metre (*1¾ oz per sq yd*) is used for the purpose, and is applied evenly to the soil for half a metre (*20 in*) each side of the row in early June.

Rhubarb being forced under the staging of a greenhouse. The black polythene with which it is normally covered, producing complete darkness, has been lifted to show the rhubarb.

After two years the crowns should be large enough to give a satisfactory yield when forced. When the autumn comes, a thermometer is laid on the soil surface near the crowns and the temperature recorded every morning. Each time the reading falls below 9.5°C (*49°F*), the *difference* is noted on a record sheet. These differences are added up each day until an accumulated total of 111 C° (*200 F°*) is reached, by which time the standard early variety 'Timperley Early' will be ready for forcing. Most other varieties will not force until a total of 167 C° (*300 F°*) has been achieved. When this number of 'cold units', as they are called, has been experienced, the crowns are lifted and placed close together on the floor of the greenhouse, packed round with soil and well watered. They are then covered with black polythene supported on a framework to give half a metre (*20 in*) or more height for the stalks to grow. Rhubarb forces satisfactorily at a temperature of about 13°C (*55°F*). 'Timperley Early' can be ready in most years at Christmas, and 'Victoria', the other main variety used for this purpose, in February and March. 'Victoria' will not force until it has had 167 cold centigrade units (*300 Fahrenheit units*). A new technique of propagating small pieces of crown under glass makes it possible to have plants ready for forcing after only one year in the field.

Chicory

Chicory, once rarely seen in shops, is now a popular winter salad available from Christmas onwards. The type used for forcing is the 'Witloof' variety, of which seed is sown in the open in May in northern England and June in southern England. The drills should be 13 mm ($\frac{1}{2}$ *in*) deep. When the seedlings emerge, they are thinned to stand 225 mm (*9 in*) apart. In October the plants are lifted, and the leaves are cut off 25 mm (*1 in*) above the top of the root. They are then dried under cover for two or three days to ensure that they become dormant. Forcing starts from October, but roots not required immediately can be stored in damp sand or soil or kept in a plastic bag in a domestic refrigerator.

The chicory roots can be forced in the greenhouse by planting in the soil and covering with black polythene in a similar manner to rhubarb. It is often convenient to force all these plants under the greenhouse staging so as not to use space which might be required for other purposes. Another method is to plant the roots in a large flower pot and to cover this with an inverted one of the same size, with black polythene to exclude light covering both. Whichever method is used, before forcing, they are thoroughly soaked. With the forcing temperature at 18°C (*65°F*), it should take three weeks to produce the blanched heads or 'chicons' as they are called. Lower temperatures such as 13°C (*55°F*) will mean that the forcing period is much longer. The chicons are cut when 150 mm (*6 in*) long.

A small batch of early potatoes in pots. These were planted back in the winter and are now nearing the point where they can be harvested.

Dandelion　　Those who want to be different may choose to force dandelions, and if so, the same methods as those described for chicory can be used, except that you are advised to obtain seed of the French improved type known as *Pissenlit amelioré à coeur plein*. In spite of the meaning of its French name, it is not noticeably diuretic.

Seakale　　Seakale is lifted from the open land in October after the foliage has died down, and all the lateral roots are trimmed off, leaving only the main root and its terminal bud. This is forced in a similar manner to chicory but at a temperature of only 13 °C (*55°F*), at which it takes some four weeks. Roots not wanted for immediate forcing are stored in moist sand or soil.

The lateral roots trimmed off the crown before forcing are sorted over, and the best of them are used as root cuttings to provide next year's crop. The cuttings should be about 150 mm (*6 in*) long, the top end of the 'thong' being cut square and the bottom end cut on the slant, in order that the top and bottom of the root can be easily identified. The cuttings are tied in bundles and stored in moist sand until March, when they are planted out 370 mm (*15 in*) apart, with their tops 37 mm (*1½ in*) below the surface. During July the shoots are reduced to one, the unwanted ones being cut away with a knife.

Asparagus　　Asparagus was forced over manure hot-beds as long ago as the seventeenth century, but today the art has almost died out. The crowns for forcing are three years old and raised from seed. The seed is sown in the spring in seed-trays in a greenhouse; the seedlings are transferred to pots, and planted out (as soon as they are well established) 225 mm (*9 in*) apart. If there is more than one row, the space between the rows should be 450 mm (*18 in*). Each spring, before growth starts, they are dressed with a compound fertiliser (18 per cent nitrogen/10 per cent phosphate/10 per cent potash or thereabouts) at 120 grams per square metre (*4 oz per sq yd*).

The crowns for forcing are dug up in October, when forcing can commence. They are laid on the floor of the greenhouse and covered with a few inches of soil, well watered in, and grown at a temperature of 21 °C (*70°F*), at which shoots for cutting should be ready in about two weeks. At 15 °C (*60°F*) the forcing period will be much longer. Forcing can be done any time from October to February.

Chapter 29

Flowers propagated and overwintered under glass

Geraniums, Marguerites, Heliotrope, fuchsia and bedding Calceolaria are prominent examples of half-hardy perennial shrubs and sub-shrubs widely used for bedding purposes, window boxes and the like. They cannot be brought through the winter satisfactorily without the help of a heated greenhouse.

Bedding Geranium (*Pelargonium zonale* – cultivars and hybrids)   **Geraniums**
Ivy-leafed Geranium (*Pelargonium peltatum* – cultivars and hybrids)

The most widely grown of all is the Zonal Pelargonium, a plant which has enjoyed a century of popularity, with some of its cultivars, 'Paul Crampel', for example, having been grown for most of this time. Because, until recent times, pelargoniums have always been propagated by cuttings, except when new varieties were being raised, viral diseases have tended to build up in stocks all over Britain. Recent work, particularly in the USA, has concentrated on the development of F1 hybrids (known as the 'Carefree varieties'), of which seed is widely offered by leading seedsmen. These hybrids result in vigorous virus-free plants that have given the species an entirely new look. Unfortunately the seed is expensive, and although not unduly difficult to raise, it is somewhat tedious when compared with the relative simplicity of cuttings. It is best to obtain seed and raise new plants, but having obtained them you may well want to keep any which you find particularly attractive from one year to the next, until they show signs of losing vigour. This means taking cuttings.

Zonal and Ivy-leaved Pelargoniums require similar conditions, and to all intents and purposes can be regarded as one. To grow successfully through the winter they require a minimum temperature of 4.5°C (*40°F*), but 7°C (*45°F*) would be better. Plants which have been flowering outdoors all summer can be lifted, potted and then brought into the greenhouse to overwinter, but it is not a method that can be recommended because it does not result in the production of very attractive plants. By far the best way is to take cuttings in August; not only does this method produce excellent plants but it is also the easiest and cheapest.

In about the middle of the month cuttings about 100–125 mm (*4–5 in*) long are taken from the flowering plants and inserted into 75 mm (*3 in*) pots, containing either John Innes Potting Compost No. 1, or a peat compost. For this particular exercise biodegradable pots are less suitable than plastic ones. It is a time-honoured practice to gather cuttings, prepare them by cutting their stem just below a node and removing a pair of leaves so that there is sufficient clean stem for insertion into the compost, and when this is done to leave them on a bench in a ventilated shed for 24 hours. The purpose of this last action is to allow the surface of the cut across the stem to harden and become less vulnerable to rotting

1. A geranium plant which was inserted as a cutting out of doors into a 75mm (*3in*) pot in early August. It rooted quickly and has been kept since the end of September on a window ledge in a dwelling-house. It is now returned to the greenhouse, the worst of the winter weather being past, and will shortly have its top removed. This will provide a cutting for a spring-rooted plant, and will cause the overwintered plant top to bush out.
2. The same plant with the top being removed to form a cutting.
3. The cutting detached.
4. The detached cutting being prepared for insertion by cutting below a node.
5. This cutting being inserted into a 75mm (*3in*) pot.
6. The inserted cutting being watered and stood on the greenhouse bench, where it will shortly take root in the bright, warm spring weather.

when in the compost. Whether this practice has ever been the subject of careful scientific investigation is difficult to ascertain, but a more logical step is to dip the cuttings into captan dust (the seed-dressing formulation) before insertion. The cuttings in their pots are then placed 'pot thick' on a standing-down bed of fine sand, normally in a frame, but without the protection of a light. Finally they are thoroughly watered. After the initial watering the cuttings are kept under a dry regime but not allowed to dry out completely.

By the end of September they should be rooted and be ready to take into the greenhouse. If kept at the temperatures mentioned above they will not grow a great deal until the longer, brighter days of spring, but then if given liquid feed they will make sturdy plants. Before they have grown too long, they should be stopped to make them bushy. Commercial growers who keep their early struck cuttings growing at 15°C (60°F) take the tops out in January to use as a second batch of cuttings. By mid-March they should

A batch of geraniums taken as August cuttings, overwintered in an unheated bedroom, and then returned to the greenhouse in March, where, after they have had their tops removed, they will soon bush out to form fine plants before going into the garden towards the end of May.

move back to a cold frame by which they will be protected at night. The frame should be lightly covered with hessian if frost is likely, but well ventilated during the day. The plants cannot leave the frame until all danger of frost has passed, which generally means the latter part of May, when they will be ready for planting out. Before the days of liquid feeding or slow-release fertilisers it would have been necessary for them to have been potted into larger pots, but this is no longer the case. They must, however, be roomed-out as they grow, so that they have every opportunity to develop to their full potential. Where heat is not available, the pots can be overwintered on window sills in the home, going out into the cold house in March.

Marguerite
(*Chrysanthemum frutescens*)

This is a plant that is not as popular now as it was a few years back, which is regrettable, for it is one of the best white-flowered daisies we have, invaluable for window boxes, hanging baskets, concrete containers and the like as well as for normal bedding purposes. Grown under glass as a perennial, it forms a bushy sub-shrub, and becomes much less attractive than if grown as a small plant from cuttings. Being an evergreen, it produces shoots suitable for cuttings the whole year round, but the best time to take them is in early September. Shoots 50–75 mm (*2–3 in*) long are cut from the parent, and prepared and inserted in the same way as chrysanthemums. The box, or pot, in which they have been inserted should be placed on the greenhouse staging and covered with a sheet of milky polythene for a few days. They should be rooted by the end of the month, and then potted into 75 mm (*3 in*) pots in which they remain all winter at a temperature not allowed to fall below 4.5°C (*40°F*). If a flower bud forms, it should be removed to make the plant bushy. From the time they are established in their own individual pots, they receive treatment identical with that of geraniums. Another method, that used by commercial growers, is to take cuttings in the spring from stock plants overwintered in the greenhouse, but this requires a temperature of 15–18°C (*60–65°F*) and is, therefore, more expensive.

Heliotrope or Cherry Pie (hybrids of *Heliotropium peruviana* and *H. corymbosum*)

This is a beautiful plant which, like the Marguerite, is grown much less often nowadays than formerly, probably because nurserymen find it rather expensive to overwinter and propagate. It is immediately susceptible to frost, but is easily rooted from cuttings taken towards the end of August or early in September. The cuttings are small compared with geraniums and Marguerites. They should be inserted into compost in a seed tray, where they can be left on the greenhouse staging until they start to grow in the spring. They are then potted into 75 mm (*3 in*) biodegradable pots and moved to frames when well established. Because of their tenderness they cannot be planted out until June, except in mild climates such as south-west England. The cool temperature régime suitable for geraniums is equally suitable for Heliotrope.

Fuchsia

There are innumerable cultivars of fuchsias which are descendants and hybrids of *Fuchsia fulgens*, a half-hardy shrub from Mexico. It is almost hardy and will sometimes survive in parts of Cornwall for several years: *Fuchsia magellanica*, which has a large number of forms and cultivars, is hardy in all but the most extreme parts of Britain. The greenhouse fuchsia is a plant very easily propagated by means of small softwood cuttings at any time of the year. For the amateur gardener, it is a question of deciding which time suits him best. If the plants are being grown for planting out in the summer in beds, or in some kind of containers, and if large plants are not required, then late summer cuttings treated in exactly the same way as Heliotropes probably constitute the best method.

A batch of fuchsias being watered by a multi-point watering system.

Alternatively fuchsias can be treated as deciduous shrubs. To accomplish this, the plants are lifted at the end of the summer and potted, or better still will be plants already in pots. They are then allowed to ripen in the autumn weather. When the first touch of frost occurs, the old leaves are shaken off and the plants are stored in frost-proof sheds or greenhouses. In the spring they will start into growth and are then taken out of mothballs, so to speak, brought into the greenhouse, pruned back quite hard and then given every encouragement to grow. They will make large plants for whatever purpose is required of them; for example, plants handled in this manner can be trained as standards to give height to bedding designs.

Finally, the enthusiast can always save some seed from the berries which are readily produced in the summer time. When they are ripe the seed is squeezed out into a bowl of water, washed clean of the pulp, and then spread out on a sheet of glass to dry. It is best sown straight away in a seed tray, while temperatures are still easily maintained at 15°C (*60°F*), at which it will germinate quite rapidly. The young seedlings are pricked-off, as soon as they can be handled, into another tray, to stand about 50 mm (*2 in*) apart from each other. If they can be established before the days shorten, they will overwinter in the tray satisfactorily at the same temperatures as all the other subjects described in this chapter. Those who cannot thus bring seedlings through the winter can save their seed until the spring. Seedlings will not be the same as their parents, and may be worse or better; but the element of surprise provides an extra interest.

Bedding Calceolaria *(Calceolaria × fruticohybrida)*

This is yet another plant of great beauty that has become much less common, probably for the same reason as Heliotrope and Marguerite – the nurserymen shrink from the cost of propagating and overwintering them. The method of propagating and overwintering is exactly the same as that for Heliotrope.

The foregoing plants do not by any means exhaust the list of those that can be treated in a similar manner where it is either an advantage or a necessity to start each flowering season with young plants. The subjects selected must be half-hardy perennials, sub-shrubs or shrubs, and normally evergreen. The list could include such plants as antirrhinums and Wallflowers, which are evergreen sub-shrubs, but does not because they are much more effectively propagated by seed. The handsome but rarely seen *Lobelia* species, *L. cardinalis, L. fulgens, L. syphalitica* and their hybrids lend themselves to this treatment, as also do *Verbena* and the Penstemons.

Chapter 30

Vegetative propagation in the greenhouse

Propagating plants, either by seed or by vegetative means, is one of the most challenging yet enjoyable activities within the whole field of horticulture. It seems to satisfy some deep creative need within most gardeners. Possibly one of the most successful associations in the world of horticulture is the International Plant Propagator's Society which has (for professional horticulturists) branches throughout the entire English-speaking world.

Clones

A plant propagated vegetatively produces a community of identical offspring known as a clone. Well-known examples of clones are 'Cox's Orange Pippin' apples, 'King Edward' potatoes and the chrysanthemum known as 'Princess Anne'. In each case, every plant in the world is, in a sense, a piece of the one original. Professional horticulturists are always careful to differentiate between clonal stocks and stock raised from seed, and to avoid the term 'parent' for the plant from which they take cuttings, always referring to it as the 'stock plant'.

In time, clones often lose their vigour; this is due to an accumulation of viral diseases. These have a debilitating effect to the point where sometimes the cultivar in question disappears from cultivation, because it is no longer worth growing. In the past, before the true nature of the problem was understood, it was accepted that a clone became 'worn out' and had to be replaced by a new one, which it was hoped would be better than the one it had superseded. However, this was not always the case. For example, nearly a century of plant breeding has not succeeded in producing a better apple, for the British palate, than 'Cox's Orange Pippin', or a more flavoursome strawberry than 'Royal Sovereign'.

Nowadays the presence of viral diseases in a clone can often be removed by the technique of micro-propagation (see Appendix VII) followed by careful testing, resulting in 'clean' stocks of clonal material. It cannot be accomplished in every case, and is worthwhile only where the economic value of the subject justifies the expense involved.

Although all members of a clone are genetically identical, it is not unknown for 'sports' to arise due to an irregularity in the process of cell division. Sports are highly valued if they give rise to attractive changes in leaf shape, flower colour or fruit colour. The different flower colours in the chrysanthemum 'Princess Anne' and the perpetual flowering carnation 'William Sim' are examples of sports of great value to the flower grower. Sports arise in various ways but the alert propagator is always on the look-out for them. Should they seem to offer promise, he will do his best to propagate the piece of tissue showing the change.

In addition to avoiding the problem of seedlings not coming 'true to type', vegetative propagation may also avoid other problems connected with propagation by seed. For example, a plant may not set seed in the local climate; seed may not be available commercially; if it is available, it may not be viable or might be too difficult to germinate and raise.

There are three main ways of propagating plants vegetatively, and all of them are practised under glass. For each type there are many methods, and within each method there are varying techniques. The table provides an outline classification of the procedures which constitute vegetative propagation.

Vegetative propagation

Mode	Method	Technique	Examples
Division	Simple division	Tearing apart Careful dissection	Many herbaceous perennials Dahlias
	Layering	Simple layering Serpentine layering Tip layering Air layering Stooling Scooping	Lilac *Lonicera – Actinidia* Blackberry and other *Rubus* species *Ficus elastica* (Rubber Plant) Apple root stocks Hyacinths
	Natural	Runners Stem tubers Cormlets Bulbils Plantlets	Strawberries Potatoes Gladiolus Lilies Kalanchöe and other succulents
Cuttings (called cuttage in USA)	Hardwoods (or leafless)	Stems Eyes	Deciduous trees and shrubs Willow – blackcurrants Vines
	Semi-ripes	Stem or tip (nodal)	Deciduous shrubs Evergreens Evergreens (treated like hardwood cuttings), e.g. lavender – rosemary
	Soft	Stem or tip (nodal) Stem or tip (internodal) Leaf – lamina Leaf – petiole Leaf-bud (single) Leaf-bud (double) Micro-propagation	Carnations – chrysanthemums – dahlias Clematis *Begonia rex* African Violet Loganberries and other *Rubus* species – *Ficus* species No specific examples – widely practised for orchids
	Root cuttings		Oriental poppy – primulas
Grafting (called graftage in USA)	Field-grafting	Whip and tongue Chip budding 'T' budding	Fruit trees – ornamental trees Fruit trees – ornamental trees Roses
	Bench-grafting	Side-veneer Splice Saddle Patch-budding	Ornamental trees – conifers Ornamental trees – conifers Rhododendron Thick barked ornamentals (under glass)
	Inarching and grafting by approach	Spliced-approach Cleft-inarching	Cucumber – tomato Apple trees

  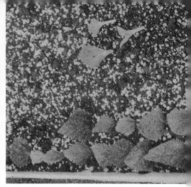

Cuttings of Leyland's Cypress (×Cupressocyparis leylandii). The specimen on the left is already well rooted; the one on the right has not yet rooted but scar tissue is forming around the cut. The wound on the cutting can just be seen above the callous.

The propagation environment

Above middle: Hydrangea cuttings. They were prepared as internodal cuttings, but in spite of this the bulk of the roots are forming around the node on the right-hand cutting. The outer leaves have been shortened to accommodate the cuttings more comfortably in the cutting bed.

Above right: A batch of leaf cuttings inserted into the rooting medium of a mist-propagation bench.

This classification is by no means complete, particularly where techniques are concerned, because their number is increasing all the time as somebody devises a better way of propagating a particular plant. It is quite impossible to deal here with all the techniques of propagation, but it is necessary to explain the propagation environment.

Any part of a plant used for propagation is conveniently described by the term *propagule*, and propagules, other than dormant ones like hardwood cuttings, have to be placed in a special environment which will keep them alive, until such time as they have regenerated their missing organs, and can function as independent plants.

All soft and semi-ripe cuttings possess leaves and other green tissues, from which they will transpire water. Transpiration is one of the major processes taking place in the plant; its roots absorb moisture, which is evaporated from the leaves. This seemingly simple process fulfills many functions. It keeps the cells full of sap so that the plant does not wilt, a condition described by botanists as 'turgidity' or 'turgor'. Of special interest to the propagator, is that the evaporation of water from the leaves removes unwanted heat from them. 'As cool as a cucumber' goes the saying, but cucumbers, or rather their leaves, are only cool because they are able to dissipate the unwanted heat they have absorbed from the sun, by using it to evaporate water.

The propagator's problem begins to become clear: his cuttings do not have roots with which to absorb water, but their leaves continue to transpire it, so they will quickly wilt unless transpiration is stopped.

Left: Examples of bench grafting under glass. The type of grafting employed is that known as the side-veneer graft. On the left is a Birch, and on the right a conifer.

Right: Bench-grafted plants (a cedar and a beech) at a later stage. In both cases the graft unions have become secure, the scions have started into full growth and the tops of the stock plants have been cut away, the cuts being clearly visible.

A batch of conifer cuttings of *Thuja occidentalis* 'Rheingold', which have been rooted in a polystyrene tray divided into compartments filled with the rooting mixture. At the bottom of the box each compartment has a hole through which it is easy to push out the rooted cutting in its plug of compost when ready for potting or planting. These cuttings have been rooted under a sheet of polythene film by the contact polythene method.

However, if it is, how can the leaves dispose of unwanted heat? They can be placed in a cold temperature, but this will prevent growth and the formation of roots; or they can be totally shaded from sunshine, but that would prevent photosynthesis and the manufacture of foodstuffs (assimilates). The propagator must find a compromise: an environment that prevents too much transpiration, keeps the leaf cool, but provides enough light for some photosynthesis to continue and enough warmth to encourage the development of roots (and whatever other organs are missing).

The first step is to reduce the moisture gradient between the atmosphere within the leaf and that outside it, which will make it more difficult for transpiration to take place.

This was done originally by using bell-jars or 'cloches', but latterly by using frames. A frame can be regarded as a device which sandwiches a thin layer of air between the soil and a glass surface. Sunshine (solar radiation) will soon cause the soil surface to evaporate water into the enclosed atmosphere, the relative humidity of which will soon rise to the point of saturation.

Cuttings within such a frame would certainly have their transpiration rate reduced, but at the same time the increasing temperature of the air would reach their thermal death point. To prevent their becoming overheated, it would be necessary to shade the frame to reduce the amount of solar radiation. If at the same time a small amount of ventilation were provided, then perhaps less shading would be needed.

The situation just described would, except for a short period of the year, place the cuttings in a situation where the temperature of the soil was too cold for growth and where the night temperature would fall too low. The advantages of transferring the frame to a greenhouse, where a much greater degree of control is possible, become self-evident. Frames in such a situation are called propagating cases.

An important part of the environment of a cutting is the medium in which the root is placed. It is quite apparent that soil does not provide the best one because it does not contain sufficient air-filled pores, nor is it sufficiently porous to permit rapid drainage. Non-calcareous silver sand on its own was used for many decades as the standard rooting-medium for cuttings, but ultimately a mixture of equal parts of peat and non-calcareous grit-sand was shown to be the most widely suitable. Some prefer mixtures of peat and perlite, but the difference is marginal.

The temperature of the rooting-medium needs to be relatively high – 18–24°C (*65–75°F*) – to bring about rapid root development. This requirement was realised very early, but until the 1870s the only means of providing it was to place the rooting-medium and propagating case on a hot-bed of fermenting manure. The introduction of pipe heating rendered this obsolete overnight, and more recently the introduction of electric heating cables has carried convenience and efficiency one step further.

We see, then, that gardeners over a long period of time have been able to work out, largely by trial and error, a method of providing an environment for cuttings which if carefully managed enabled them to be kept alive until they produced roots. Matters, however, did not stand still. In the 1950s we had the advent of mist-propagation: this mechanised the whole propagation routine and was thought, for many years, to have rendered the propagation-case obsolete. Mist-propagation (or even just 'mist') is gardening jargon for intermittent misting apparatus for plant propagation.

It is an arrangement whereby a line of nozzles is mounted above a bed of cuttings. At self-regulating intervals, the nozzles produce a mist-like spray which falls upon the cuttings, moistening the leaves with a thin film of water. The bed of cuttings is unshaded, and solar radiation soon provides the leaves with sufficient surplus heat to dry-off this film of water. At the moment they become dry, a sensor signals the control mechanism to release another burst of mist, and the cycles of wetting and drying are repeated. The consequence is that the leaves of the cuttings are kept permanently moist, and are able to dispose of their surplus heat by evaporating moisture placed upon them, rather than by using their own, thus maintaining 'turgor' while exposed to full sunlight. The fineness of the mist and the small quantity of water used prevents saturation of the rooting-medium, yet at the same time stops it from drying out.

Three kinds of sensor have been developed:

1. The so-called 'artificial leaf' which consists of two carbon electrodes separated by insulating material. When the surface of this is wet a small

A burst of mist from the nozzles of a mist-propagation bench. These nozzles are controlled by a sensor located among the cuttings which causes a burst of mist to occur whenever the leaves of the cuttings become dry.

current flows between the electrodes, but as the surface dries the current ceases to flow, and its cessation is relayed as a signal to the controller which then energises a solenoid valve which opens to allow a burst of mist. The sensor is placed among the cuttings, and to a certain extent simulates their wetting and drying properties; hence its name.

2. A mechanical switch operated by a sensitive balance. One side of the balance is an absorbent pad. When this is wet the balance is tilted in its direction, but as it dries the balance gradually moves to the other, so making an electrical contact and sending a signal to the controller.

3. A sensor which integrates the light energy falling on it; when this reaches a certain pre-determined but adjustable level, the controller is signalled.

All three have their limitations; none is ideal.

The advent of 'mist' certainly extended the range of plants that could be propagated, and significantly reduced the time taken to root them.

Although mist-propagation kits are available to the amateur, they are not in the writer's opinion suited to his needs. To work effectively they need water pressures between 315 and 420 kN/m² (*45–60 lb/sq in*), and these are rarely available. Most water authorities will not permit installations to be fitted direct to the water supply; they insist upon an interrupted supply which in turn necessitates the installation of a pressure vessel and pump; finally the electrical supply adds a further measure of expense.

The next major development in vegetative propagation came from the use of polythene film. The success with which amateur gardeners could root cuttings in flower pots, covered by plastic bags held in position by an elastic band, had not gone unnoticed either by the nurseryman or the research worker.

In the 1970s nurserymen were beginning to root their later summer and autumn (semi-ripe) cuttings under sheets of polythene film actually in contact with their leaves. This became known as the 'contact-polythene' system, and offers a very simple and inexpensive means of providing a propagation environment.

When the cuttings have been inserted into the rooting medium and covered with the polythene, the entrapped air rapidly develops a high relative humidity. In due course there is a characteristic layer of water droplets formed on the underside of the polythene. This is very important, because not only does it assist in shading the cuttings, but also in periods of stronger sunshine this droplet layer will partially evaporate, thus absorbing some of the unwanted solar energy. Day-time temperatures under the polythene are, of course, higher than that of the air above the film which thus constitutes a cooler surface on which condensation can occur.

Propagation beds to be covered with polythene were originally provided with bottom heat in the traditional fashion, but it is now thought that this is not essential. The bench on which the bed is formed is covered with a sheet of expanded polystyrene and then covered with a depth of sand retained by low walls, little higher than the bed, and also lined with expanded polystyrene. This results in a rooting medium insulated from heat loss during the night, and yet receiving all the heat it requires during the day from solar radiation.

The contact-polythene method can also be used in cold frames outdoors. The frame has a sand base about 150 mm (*6 in*) deep, with the rooting

Cuttings of Leyland's Cypress being rooted under a sheet of polythene film, which lies directly on the cuttings, the method being described as 'contact polythene'.

medium spread over it. The cuttings are inserted and covered with polythene, and then glass lights are placed on the frame which is, in effect, double-glazed. This is essentially a summer and early autumn method, ideal for conifers, semi-ripe cuttings and deciduous shrubs, evergreen shrubs such as heathers, hollies and many others. The cuttings are taken from June until early October. In the following spring they should be rooted and ready for growing-on.

There are some other important points concerned with cuttings. Perhaps the chief is the use of so-called root-promoting hormones. These are based on indol-butyric acid, and are readily available as branded products into which the base of the cutting is dipped before insertion. Though quite unnecessary for many cuttings, they are of great advantage when rooting the 'shyer' subjects, for which their use should become a matter of routine.

Another practice, over which an air of mystery hangs, is that of 'wounding' cuttings. The normal method of preparing stem cuttings is to cut through below a node (the thickened part of the stem from which leaves and buds arise) with a sharp, thin knife: knives made from razor blades are ideal. In the case of woody subjects, particularly conifers, a small sliver is pared away at the base of the stem, about 10 mm (*0.4 in*) long, thus giving the appearance of a church window. The effectiveness of wounding is beyond question, but the cause of its effectiveness is not clear. One plausible explanation is that the water-conducting tubes in the stem of the cuttings become blocked at their bases by bacteria in the same way as those of cut-flowers. The wound has the effect of providing an entry point for water above the point of blockage.

Cuttings, until their exposed tissues have been covered with callus, are vulnerable to infection by various fungi and bacteria, and it should be standard practice to dip their ends into a fungicidal seed dressing. Where hormone treatments are being used it is possible to buy combined hormone and fungicidal powders.

An even more thorough procedure is to dip the cuttings, before insertion, into a benlate spray (1 g of branded product per litre) or a captan spray (1.3 g of branded product per litre), and then to drench the rooting medium with the same solution.

Shading

The final point to make about cuttings being rooted under contact-polythene, which must be the most attractive method for the amateur, is that of shading. This subject has been studied scientifically and may be summarised thus: The metric measurement used to express the total light environment of the cutting is that of megajoules per metre squared (MJ/m^2); here there is no convenient imperial equivalent. Cuttings root quite satisfactorily provided that the integral light does not fall below 1.5 MJ/m^2. Integral light in the UK varies from about 2 to 20 MJ/m^2 from mid-winter to mid-summer; from this must be deducted the losses incurred by the glass and polythene through which the light must be transmitted to reach the cuttings; superimposed upon it must be the variations occurring regularly throughout the day and (irregularly) from day to day. Experiments have shown that cuttings maintained at a level of integral light around 3 MJ/m^2 have done extremely well, and have not suffered from high-temperature effects on the one hand nor low-light effects on the other. To achieve a steady regime of 3 MJ/m^2, shading at varying levels is required from mid-February to the end of October, and it would be impossible to provide this without an automatic system controlled by a light-sensitive sensor. For most amateur gardeners this is too sophisticated a system, and a more rough-and-ready one is more appropriate.

Such a system requires that wires are arranged over the propagation bed at a height of 500 mm (*20 in*) to support a layer of cloth. The cloth chosen should be of a weave that supplies 40 per cent shade. From April to August the glass above the bed is shaded with a glasshouse-shading compound. From March to October a decision must be made daily as to whether it is going to be bright or dull. If the latter, then no shading will be required other than that provided by the shading of the glass. If the former, then one layer of cloth is needed on the wire supports from March to October, and two layers from April to August.

Shading requirements for cuttings under contact-polythene

	Jan	Feb	Mar	Apr	May	Jun	July	Aug	Sept	Oct	Nov	Dec
Dull day			— — — — — — — — — — — — — — — —									
Bright day		— — — — — — — — — — — — — — — — — — —									

— — — — — = whitewash on glass

———— = 40 per cent shade cloth

Dr K. Loach of the Glasshouse Crops Research Institute, who devised the shading routines, defines a bright day as one which is 50 per cent brighter than an average day, and a dull one as 50 per cent duller than the average. The shading period with cloth is 0800–1600 hrs. The same system can be operated with frames outdoors, with the cloth laid directly onto the glass.

When cuttings are being rooted in greenhouses it is usually more convenient, though not essential, to put the rooting medium into containers and to stand these on the sand. If the containers are seed trays, they should have extra holes drilled in their bases to increase the contact between the sand and the medium. (The sum of the area of the holes in the container should be equal to about 25 per cent of its base.)

Root cuttings

While leafy cuttings are by far and away the most common propagules used in greenhouses there are others; root-cuttings are very useful for many plants which are able to produce buds on their roots. Root-cuttings fall into two categories:

1. from plants with thicker roots, such as:
    Clerodendron trichotomum
    Ailanthus altissima (Tree of Heaven)
    Romneya coulteri
    Passiflora (Passion flowers)
2. from those with thin roots, such as:
    Primula denticulata and its cultivars
    Geranium sanguineum and its cultivars
    Erodium species

The larger roots are cut into pieces 40–50 mm (*1½–2 in*) long and placed vertically into 75 mm (*3 in*) pots containing John Innes No. 1 Potting Compost or a loamless potting compost. The tops of the cuttings should be level with the top of the compost, and then covered with a few millimetres

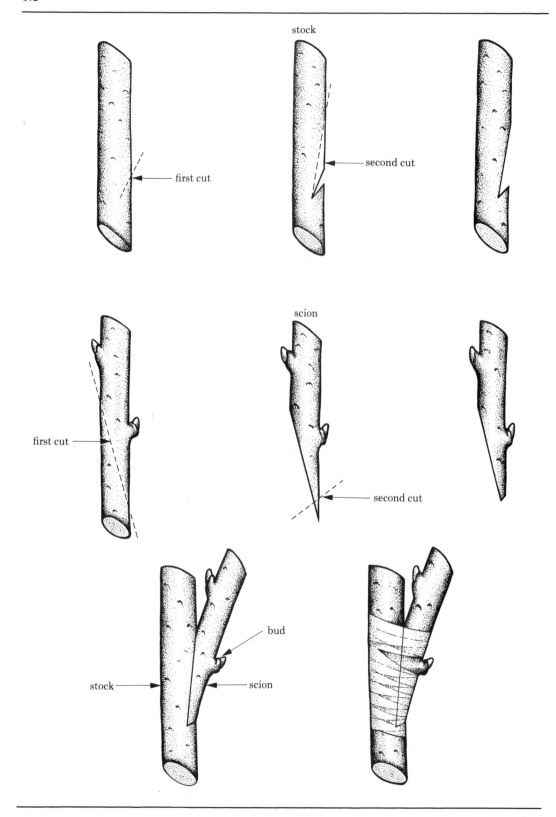

stock

first cut

second cut

scion

first cut

second cut

bud

stock

scion

of sharp sand. After watering they are placed on a bed of sand. When the shoots are growing strongly they are ready for planting out or potting into larger pots.

The thin roots are cut into pieces about 25 mm (*1 in*) long and dibbled into seed trays containing a potting compost. If the nature of the root makes this too difficult, they can be laid onto compost horizontally and covered with a few millimetres of compost.

Both pots and boxes should be kept moist and can be covered with contact-polythene until shoots appear.

Root cuttings are usually prepared and inserted during the dormant season when it is more convenient, but some argue that it is best done in the peak of the growing season when buds develop on the roots very quickly.

Very many named cultivars of ornamental trees are propagated in greenhouses by grafting. Because the work is done on the greenhouse staging or on a work-top the method is known as bench-grafting. The most popular technique is a type of graft known as a side veneer graft (see Fig. 39). Many other kinds are recommended in the established literature, but modern propagators are tending to use it universally.

The procedure for deciduous trees, such as a Cut-leaved Beech (*Fagus sylvatica* 'Heterophylla'), is as follows. A well-developed seedling of Common Beech is lifted in February and brought into the greenhouse. A one-year-old shoot of the Cut-leaved Beech is brought in at the same time. A scion is prepared and grafted onto a suitable place on the stem of the seedling. The graft is secured, and the grafted plant potted and placed in a propagating case or polythene tent until the buds on both stock and scion have opened. It is then removed from the case or tent and placed on the greenhouse staging. A little later, the stock is trimmed back and the ties on the union removed. Finally, all the rootstock above the union is removed, and the young plant hardened-off.

With evergreens, and conifers in particular, the procedure is much the same, except that in such cases the rootstock has to be established in the pot for some considerable time before grafting, and it is not necessary, in all cases, to use a propagating case.

Fig. 39 *(opposite page):* side-veneer graft. Top row: preparation of the stock. Middle row: preparation of the scion. Bottom row: uniting the two and tying the graft around a bud.

Grafting

1. *Ficus elastica*, the so-called Rubber plant, upon which it is intended to make an air layer. The stem of the plant has been wounded by the removal of some of the rind; this hastens the rooting process. The wounded area is treated with a hormone rooting powder.
2. The same plant with moist sphagnum moss wrapped around the wounded area and secured with string.
3. The sphagnum moss is wrapped around with polythene film which is securely tied in position. This polythene film allows oxygen and carbon dioxide to permeate through to the plant stem, but prevents the loss of moisture.
4. The same plant from a distance. This method of air layering does not have to be practised on the central stem of the plant as here. It is usually done on a lateral shoot in order to produce a new plant without decapitating the parent or stock plant.

Air-layering

A description of an ingenious method of layering ends this brief review of propagation. Air-layering is used for plants that are difficult to propagate by other means. The method is extremely simple: a young shoot on the stock-plant is selected, and on a clean length of its stem a wound is made; rooting hormone is applied to the area and then a handful of moist sphagnum moss is tied around; this is then covered with polythene which is tied to the stem above and below the sphagnum moss. If a sleeve made from a plastic bag can be slid onto the stem instead of using a sheet of plastic, so much the better. In due course the sphagnum moss becomes filled with roots, and in the spring or early summer the layer can be detached, potted and nursed in a propagating case until established.

Summary

Vegetative propagation is an immense subject, making up a large part of horticulture. In this chapter the principles which govern its practice have been briefly described, but the practical details of propagating particular plants have had to be omitted.

It may be summed up as follows:

1. Most plants are propagated vegetatively by leafy cuttings of one sort or another.

2. Such cuttings need a special environment which can be provided by covering cuttings with a sheet of thin polythene film.

3. Shading is necessary to prevent overheating; this can be provided by a combination of shade cloth and whitewashing.

4. Bottom heat has for long been considered essential for propagating beds in greenhouses and can be provided by means of electric soil-warming cables, thermostatically controlled.

5. Root-promoting hormones are necessary for shy-rooting plants.

6. Prophylactic treatment with fungicide of cuttings and the medium in which they are growing is highly advisable.

7. Wounding treatments are helpful for woody plants, particularly conifers.

8. Rooting media must have a good number of air-filled pores (30–50 per cent), and must be well drained.

9. For semi-ripe leafy cuttings in summer and autumn, cold frames outdoors may be used as an alternative to beds in greenhouses.

10. Bench grafting is a useful propagation technique requiring the convenience in many cases of a propagating case with bottom heat or, as a cheap alternative, a polythene tent.

11. Root-cuttings are an overlooked and under-used method of propagating many plants.

12. Air-layering is a simple propagation technique for plants which are difficult to propagate in any other way.

Heat requirement for greenhouses

In order to maintain a given temperature in a greenhouse the heat input must at all times equal the rate at which the house is losing heat. Heat loss is constantly changing, the determinants being windspeed, the clearness of the night sky, and whether the glass overlaps are sealed by moisture. Any estimate of heat loss must allow for the most extreme conditions which could occur, and then strike some compromise between them and what is probable.

This is done by dividing the country into regions with similar climatic patterns and deciding upon an outside base temperature. This is the lowest outdoor temperature in that particular region likely to persist for a protracted period of time, rather than for only two or three hours. In England, for example:

	°C	°F
Southern England	−4.5	24
London and the East	−5.5	22
South-west	−1	30
Yorkshire and North-east	−6.5	20
North-west	−5.5	22

Check for your own locality by consulting the local horticultural advisor of the Agricultural Development and Advisory Service (ADAS) of the Ministry of Agriculture and Fisheries, in Great Britain, or similar advisory bodies in other countries.

Once the outside base temperature has been determined it must then be decided what is the lowest temperature required to be maintained in the greenhouse. This is best referred to as the minimum night temperature, because if it can be maintained at night, when there is no assistance whatever from the sun, it can easily be maintained during the day. If the outside base temperature is subtracted from the greenhouse minimum night temperature, we have what is called the temperature lift.

The heat loss through the surface of a greenhouse is estimated as being

8 watts per metre squared per C° difference between inside and outside temperatures

(1.4 British thermal units per hour per square foot per F° difference between inside and outside temperatures)

To obtain the total heat loss per hour it is necessary to calculate the surface area of the greenhouse. As this includes the brick wall on which the house may stand the area of the wall is divided by half to allow for its lower thermal transmission. The total figure is called the equivalent glass area. Calculate it as follows:

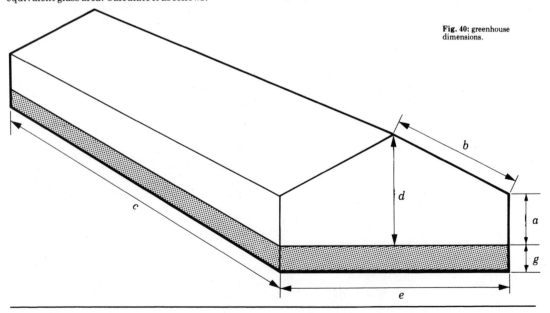

Fig. 40: greenhouse dimensions.

area of roof plus glass walls
$= 2 \times$ (height of glass walls (a) + roof slope (b)) $\times$ length (c) = $\qquad$ x
area of gable ends plus end glass walls
$=$ (height of glass to ridge (d) + height of glass wall (a)) $\times$ width (e) = $\qquad$ y
half area of brick walls
$=$ height of brick walls (g) $\times$ (length (c) + width (e)) = $\qquad$ z

$$x + y + z$$

If we give values to the dimensions, e.g.

a	=	1 m	$3\frac{1}{2}$ ft
b	=	5 m	17 ft
c	=	30 m	100 ft
d	=	3.5 m	$11\frac{1}{2}$ ft
e	=	9 m	30 ft
g	=	0.5 m	$1\frac{1}{2}$ ft

then the equivalent glass area of the house in Fig. 40 would be:

Area of roof and glass walls
$= 2 \times (1 + 5) \times 30$ $= 360$ m^2
or $2 \times (3\frac{1}{2} + 17) \times 100$ =   *4100 sq ft*
Area of gable ends + end glass walls
$= (3.5 + 1) \times 9$ $= 40.5$ m^2
or $(11\frac{1}{2} + 3\frac{1}{2}) \times 30$ =   *450 sq ft*
Half area of brick walls
$= 0.5 \times (30 + 9)$ $= 19.5$ m^2
or $1\frac{1}{2} \times (100 + 30)$ =   *195 sq ft*

                   420 m^2 *4745 sq ft*

The heat requirement of the house is

equivalent glass area in m^2 (*sq ft*) $\times$ temperature lift in C$^\circ$ (*F$^\circ$*) $\times$ F

where F, the conversion factor, is 8×10^{-3} kW/m^2/C$^\circ$ (*1.4 Btu/sq ft/F$^\circ$/hr*). The metric calculation gives the answer in kilowatts, and the imperial calculation gives the answer in British thermal units per hour.
    Suppose that the greenhouse used as our example is in Yorkshire, where the outside base temperature is −6.5°C (*20°F*). If it is to have a heating system which will maintain a minimum night temperature of 15.5°C (*60°F*), we can calculate that the temperature lift required will be:

$$15.5° + 6.5° = 22C° \quad (60° - 20° = 40F°)$$

and its heat requirement will be

$$420 \times 22 \times 8 \times 10^{-3} = 74 \text{ kW} \quad (4745 \times 40 \times 1.4 = 265{,}720 \text{ Btu/hr}).$$

    If this amount of heat is to be provided by a solid-fuel boiler it is usually necessary to have a boiler with a heat capacity one-third greater than the heat requirement of the greenhouse. This allows for the various unavoidable losses of heat normally referred to as boiler inefficiency.

For further details see MAFF Bulletin No. 115, *Commercial Glasshouses*.

Thus the boiler capacity required would be

$$74 \times 1.33 = 99 \text{ kW} \quad (265{,}720 \times 1.33 = 354{,}293 \text{ Btu/hr})$$

    Boilers are, of course, made in discrete sizes, and the one suitable would have a capacity not less than that required – say 400,000 Btu/hr or 120 kW. If oil or gas boilers are used the efficiency may be higher. Professional advice is required before purchase is made.
    The next step in installing a heating system is knowing how much pipe of any particular diameter is needed to deliver the amount of heat required into the house. The thermal transmission of metal pipes depends upon their diameter, the temperature of the water or steam inside them and the temperature at which the house is kept. In a hot water system it is usual for the heat to leave the boiler, when the system is working to the full, at a temperature of 82°C (*180°F*) and return at one of 71°C (*160°F*) giving an average temperature of 76.5°C (*170°F*). At this temperature the thermal emission of various pipes is as follows:

100 mm (*4 in*) cast iron	277 watts/metre	*288 Btu/ft/hr*
50 mm (*2 in*) mild steel	174 watts/metre	*180 Btu/ft/hr*
37 mm (*1½ in*) mild steel	129 watts/metre	*134 Btu/ft/hr*
31 mm (*1¼ in*) mild steel	104 watts/metre	*107 Btu/ft/hr*
25 mm (*1 in*) mild steel	93 watts/metre	*96 Btu/ft/hr*

These figures have to be adjusted up or down slightly if it is intended to maintain higher or lower temperatures in a greenhouse, but the difference in the amount of pipe required in a small greenhouse is neither here nor there.

The amount of pipe required is the heat requirement of the house divided by the thermal emission of the pipe. Thus in the example chosen the amount of pipe required would be:

	metres	feet
100 mm (*4 in*) cast iron	267	*923*
50 mm (*2 in*) mild steel	425	*1476*
37 mm (*1½ in*) mild steel	574	*1983*
31 mm (*1¼ in*) mild steel	712	*2483*
25 mm (*1 in*) mild steel	796	*2768*

As can be seen, for smaller diameters of pipe a considerable length has to be accommodated within the house, e.g. 31 mm (*1¼ in*) pipe would have at least twelve flows up the house and twelve returns. To reduce the amount of such pipe, gilled pipe, which has a much greater thermal emission per unit length, is often used.

Fuel required to maintain a minimum temperature of 7 °C (*45°F*) throughout the year in small greenhouses

Size	Coal (kg) (70% efficiency)	Oil (litres) (80% efficiency)	Electricity (kW-hr) (100% efficiency)	Natural gas (therms) (100% efficiency)	Bottled gas (propane) (cu ft) (100% efficiency)
1.8 × 2.4 m *6 × 8 ft*	158	103	860	30	1174
2.4 × 3.7 m *8 × 12 ft*	226	146	1227	42	1675
2.4 × 4.6 m *8 × 15 ft*	330	213	1796	62	2452
3 × 3.8 m *10 × 12½ ft*	308	199	1674	58	2284
3 × 4.6 m *10 × 15 ft*	399	260	2162	74	2951
3 × 5.3 m *10 × 17½ ft*	448	291	2426	83	3312
3 × 6.1 m *10 × 20 ft*	495	323	2689	92	3670
3 × 7.6 m *10 × 25 ft*	599	383	3218	110	4392
3 × 9.1 m *10 × 30 ft*	690	446	3746	128	5113
3.7 × 6.1 m *12 × 20 ft*	559	360	3037	104	4145
3.7 × 7.6 m *12 × 25 ft*	666	432	3615	124	4934
3.7 × 9.1 m *12 × 30 ft*	773	496	4193	144	5727
4.6 × 9.1 m *15 × 30 ft*	869	560	4713	161	6433

Fuel required to maintain a minimum temperature of 15°C (*60°F*) during March, April, May and June in small greenhouses

Size	Coal (kg)	Oil (litres)	Electricity (kW-hr)	Natural gas (therms)	Bottled gas (propane) (cu ft)
1.8 × 2.4 m *6 × 8 ft*	312	202	1693	58	2311
2.4 × 3.7 m *8 × 12 ft*	446	288	2416	83	3298
2.4 × 4.6 m *8 × 15 ft*	689	444	3733	128	5095
3 × 3.8 m *10 × 12½ ft*	653	421	3541	121	4832
3 × 4.6 m *10 × 15 ft*	785	507	4257	146	5810
8 × 5.3 m *10 × 17½ ft*	882	568	4777	163	6520
3 × 6.1 m *10 × 20 ft*	977	630	5295	181	7227
3 × 7.6 m *10 × 25 ft*	1169	754	6336	217	8648
3 × 9.1 m *10 × 30 ft*	1361	877	7376	252	10067
3.7 × 6.1 m *12 × 20 ft*	1103	711	5986	205	8170
3.7 × 7.6 m *12 × 25 ft*	1313	847	7118	243	9715
3.7 × 9.1 m *12 × 30 ft*	1523	982	8257	282	11270
4.6 × 9.1 m *15 × 30 ft*	1712	1105	9282	317	12669

The cost ratio is, very approximately,

coal	18
oil	38
electricity	100
natural gas	21
propane	54

(based on UK fuel costs at November 1981).

Fuel required to maintain a minimum temperature of 18°C (*65°F*) throughout the year in small greenhouses

Size	Coal (kg)	Oil (litres)	Electricity (kW-hr)	Natural gas (therms)	Bottled gas (propane) (cu ft)
1.8 × 2.4 m *6 × 8 ft*	1825	1178	9904	338	13517
2.4 × 3.7 m *8 × 12 ft*	2604	1680	14132	483	19288
2.4 × 4.6 m *8 × 15 ft*	3075	1985	16686	570	22774
3 × 3.8 m *10 × 12½ ft*	2908	1876	15780	539	21537
3 × 4.6 m *10 × 15 ft*	4589	2960	24719	844	33737
3 × 5.3 m *10 × 17½ ft*	5149	3323	27944	954	38138
3 × 6.1 m *10 × 20 ft*	5707	3683	30974	1057	42274
3 × 7.6 m *10 × 25 ft*	6830	4408	37066	1265	50588
3 × 9.1 m *10 × 30 ft*	7950	5131	43147	1473	58888
3.7 × 6.1 m *12 × 20 ft*	6446	4160	34981	1194	47743
3.7 × 7.6 m *12 × 25 ft*	7673	6302	41641	1421	56832
3.7 × 9.1 m *12 × 30 ft*	8900	7309	48302	1649	65923
4.6 × 9.1 m *15 × 30 ft*	10004	8717	54296	1853	74104

Appendix II

The preparation of liquid feeds

1. The preparation of liquid feeds, as opposed to the purchase of ready-mixed preparations either as powders or solutions, offers three advantages:
a. It is considerably cheaper.
b. Any nutrient ratio can be achieved.
c. Any concentration of feed can be obtained from a standard dilution rate.

2. In the past, various dilution rates for stock solutions have been used, but the Glasshouse Crops Research Institute has long advised a standard dilution rate of 1 in 200, varying the concentration of the stock solution accordingly. All the calculations that follow are based on this procedure.

3. The concentration of liquid feeds is expressed in terms of parts per million of nutrient (ppm). To give an immediate impression of the concentration of a particular feed, the total nutrient concentration is frequently stated together with the nutrient ratio. For example:
A widely used feed for vigorous pot plants contains
500 ppm of nutrient with N and K_2O in the ratio of 2 : 1
ppm of N $= 500 \times \frac{2}{3} = 333$
ppm of $K_2O = 500 \times \frac{1}{3} = 166$
N = Nitrogen K_2O = Potash $K_2O \times 0.83$ = Potassium.

4. The fertilisers used for liquid feeding must be soluble and free from insoluble impurities. It may be necessary occasionally to strain stock solutions through fine gauze to remove any insoluble impurities. Those in normal use are as follows:
a. Potassium nitrate (KNO_3) 13%N : 46% K_2O – the most widely used potassium source and one which will not affect the pH of the compost.
b. Potassium sulphate (K_2SO_4) 48% K_2O. This is a single source of potassium. Its sulphate ions will lock up calcium as calcium sulphate, and reduce the amount of exchangeable bases in a compost, so preventing its pH rising under the influence of hard water. It is the preferred form for loamless composts.
c. Ammonium nitrate (NH_4NO_3) 35%N. This is the normal substance used for increasing the nitrogen content of a feed without adding any but ammonium and nitrate ions. The nitrification of its ammonium ions leads to the removal of two calcium ions.
d. Urea ($CO(NH_2)_2$) 46%N. This may be regarded as a straight alternative to ammonium nitrate in all respects. It must be guaranteed free from the phytotoxic impurity biuret. It is less readily obtainable, and now has been more or less superseded by ammonium nitrate.
e. Ammonium sulphate (($NH_4)_2SO_4$) 21%N. This is generally used for feeds for tomatoes, whose flavour it is said to improve. Its nitrification can immobilise four calcium ions, and its use may be advisable for increasing the nitrogen content of feeds for use on loamless composts and where hard water may cause the pH to rise.
f. Mono-ammonium phosphate ($NH_4H_2PO_4$) 11%N: 48% soluble P_2O_5. This is used for providing phosphate to a feed on the comparatively rare occasions when it is needed.
NB The ammonium metallic phosphates such as Magamp have no real use in the preparation of liquid feeds.
g. Magnesium sulphate ($MgSO_4$) 20% Mg. This may be needed to prevent magnesium deficiency, particularly for sensitive crops such as those of the family Solanaceae, e.g. tomato, pepper etc.
h. Aluminium sulphate $Al_2(SO_4)_3$. Used for the 'blueing' of hydrangeas.

5. In order to prepare a stock solution, the quantities of the various fertilisers that must be dissolved in one litre (*one gallon*) of water must be calculated.
a. In grams for preparing stock solutions in litres using the formula

$$\frac{\text{ppm of nutrient required} \times 20}{\text{percentage of nutrient in fertiliser}}$$

to prepare a stock solution for a liquid feed containing 166 ppm of potash (K_2O) using potassium nitrate

$\dfrac{166 \times 20}{46} = 72$ grams (to nearest gram) are required per litre

b. In ounces for preparing stock solutions in gallons using the formula

$$\frac{\text{ppm of nutrient required} \times 16}{5 \times \text{percentage of nutrient in fertiliser}}$$

$\dfrac{166 \times 16}{5 \times 46} = 11\frac{1}{2}$ oz of potassium nitrate (to nearest $\frac{1}{2}$ oz) are required per gallon

c. When it is necessary to use fertilisers like potassium nitrate which contain two nutrients, i.e. in this case nitrogen and potassium (K_2O), it is necessary to calculate first the amount of potassium nitrate needed to provide the correct amount of potash as in (a) or (b) above and then to calculate the ppm of nitrogen this will provide. This amount of nitrogen must then be subtracted from the total amount of nitrogen required in ppm if this is greater than the amount already provided by the potassium nitrate.

For grams use the formula:

$$\frac{\text{percentage of nutrient in fertiliser} \times \text{amount of fertiliser}}{20}$$

from example (a) above

$\dfrac{13 \times 72}{20} = 47$ ppm of nitrogen (to nearest ppm)

are provided by 72 grams of potassium nitrate

For ounces use the formula:

$$\frac{\text{percentage of nutrient in fertiliser} \times 5 \times \text{amount of fertiliser}}{16}$$

from example (b) above

$\dfrac{13 \times 5 \times 11\frac{1}{2}}{16} = 47$ ppm of nitrogen (to nearest ppm)

are provided by $11\frac{1}{2}$ oz of potassium nitrate.

6. A worked example illustrates the method of calculation:

Using potassium nitrate and ammonium nitrate, calculate to the nearest gram ($\frac{1}{2}$ oz) the quantities of each to be dissolved in one litre (*one gallon*) of water to make a stock solution which when diluted 200 times will contain 333 ppm of nitrogen and 166 ppm of potash (K_2O)

Amount of potassium nitrate required =

$\dfrac{166 \times 20}{46} = 72$ grams $\qquad or \quad \dfrac{166 \times 16}{5 \times 46} = 11\frac{1}{2}\,oz$

This will provide

$\dfrac{13 \times 72}{20} = 47$ ppm nitrogen $\qquad \dfrac{13 \times 5 \times 23}{16 \times 2} = 47\,ppm\ nitrogen$

ppm of nitrogen still required $= 333 - 47 = 286$

Amount of ammonium nitrate required =

$\dfrac{286 \times 20}{35} = 164$ grams $\qquad or \quad \dfrac{286 \times 16}{5 \times 35} = 26\,oz$

So the quantities required are:

Potassium nitrate	72 grams	*11½ oz*	
Ammonium nitrate	164 grams	*26 oz*	
Water	1 litre	*1 gallon*	

7. The same method may be used where three nutrients are required, as in the following example:

Calculate in grams per litre (*ounces per gallon*) the quantities of ammonium nitrate, potassium nitrate and mono-ammonium phosphate required to make a stock solution which when diluted 200 times will provide a feed containing 600 ppm of total nutrient with N: soluble P_2O_5: K_2O in the ratio 2:1:1.

ppm of N $= 600 \times \frac{1}{2} \times 300$

ppm of soluble $P_2O_5 = 600 \times \frac{1}{4} = 150$

ppm of $K_2O = 600 \times \frac{1}{4} = 150$

Amount of potassium nitrate required =

$\dfrac{150 \times 20}{46} = 65\,\text{grams}$
 or $\dfrac{150 \times 16}{5 \times 46} = 10\tfrac{1}{2}\,oz$

This will provide

$\dfrac{13 \times 65}{20} = 43\,\text{ppm nitrogen}$
 or $\dfrac{13 \times 5 \times 10\tfrac{1}{2}}{16} = 43\,ppm\ nitrogen$

Amount of mono-ammonium phosphate =

$\dfrac{150 \times 20}{48} = 63\,\text{grams}$
 or $\dfrac{150 \times 16}{5 \times 48} = 10\tfrac{1}{2}\,oz$

This will provide

$\dfrac{11 \times 63}{20} = 35\,\text{ppm nitrogen}$
 or $\dfrac{11 \times 5 \times 10\tfrac{1}{2}}{16} = 36\,ppm\ nitrogen$

ppm of nitrogen still required =

$300 - (43 + 35) = 222$
 or $300 - (43 + 36) = 221$

Amount of ammonium nitrate required =

$\dfrac{222 \times 20}{35} = 127\,\text{grams}$
 or $\dfrac{221 \times 16}{5 \times 36} = 20\,oz$

So the quantities required are:

Ammonium nitrate	127 grams	*20 oz*
Potassium nitrate	65 grams	*10½ oz*
Mono-ammonium phosphate	63 grams	*10½ oz*
Water	1 litre	*1 gallon*

8. With the concentrations normally used for stock solutions, solubility problems are rarely encountered. If they do occur the quantities of fertilisers required should be dissolved into two litres (*2 gallons*) of water and the dilution rate set at 100 times. Potassium nitrate is soluble to the extent of about 0.22 kg per litre (*2¼ lb per gallon*) in cold water. The other chemicals have greater solubility.

9. Nutrient ratios in common use range in simple proportions from $1N:3K_2O$ to $2N:1K_2O$. Feeds applied to crops in soil usually range from $1N:3K_2O$ to $1N:1K_2O$, while for plants in containers ratios with N in excess of K_2O, e.g. $2N:1K_2O$, are common. This may be explained by the fact that in soil large amounts of NO_3^- (nitrates) would lead quickly to high conductivity (high soluble salt concentration) resulting in restriction of plant growth, whereas in a container leaching of nitrates prevents high conductivity.

10. Total nutrient concentrations may be as low as 300 ppm for slow-growing plants in winter, and as high as 800 ppm for container-grown shrubs in summer.

11. Liquid feeding when growth is fast (at the nutrient concentrations mentioned in (9) above) should be continual, i.e. with *every* watering.

12. Investigation of the nutrient needs of plants in soil or containers have been thorough for all the crops covered by the Agricultural Development and Advisory Service (ADAS) 'Blueprints', but for others, gardeners need to be guided by experience and only general recommendations can be given, e.g. vigorous pot plants in summer $N2:K_2O1$ total nutrient 300 ppm; these concentrations possibly reduced in winter, although as watering is then less frequent care to avoid malnutrition is necessary.

13. With loamless composts in hard water areas pH values tend to rise and result in lime-induced chlorosis and to counteract this liquid feeds which lock up calcium as calcium sulphate or cause it to be leached as calcium bicarbonate are necessary. Potassium sulphate and ammonium sulphate are used for this purpose.

14. Trace elements are included in many proprietory feeds, but are superfluous if a micro-nutrient frit has been added to the compost.

Some common liquid feeds (dilution always 1 in 200)

1. Potassium nitrate   150 grams $1\frac{1}{2}$ lb
   Water   1 litre   1 gallon
   Nutrient content = 105 ppm nitrogen, 335 ppm potash K_2O.
   Nutrient ratio = $1N:3K_2O$
   Used for newly planted tomatoes in soil.

2. Potassium nitrate   150 grams $1\frac{1}{2}$ lb
   Ammonium nitrate   38 grams   6 oz
   Water   1 litre   1 gallon
   Nutrient content = 170 ppm nitrogen, 335 ppm potash K_2O
   Nutrient ratio = $1N:2K_2O$
   Used for tomatoes and other plants in soil through the main part of the growing season.

3. Potassium nitrate   150 grams $1\frac{1}{2}$ lb
   Ammonium nitrate   70 grams   11 oz
   Water   1 litre   1 gallon
   Nutrient content = 225 ppm nitrogen, 335 ppm potash K_2O
   Nutrient ratio = $1N:1\frac{1}{2}K_2O$

4. Ammonium nitrate   6 grams   10 oz
   Water   1 litre   1 gallon
   Nutrient content = 110 ppm nitrogen
   Used on cucumber on straw bales for first three weeks after planting.

5. Ammonium nitrate   132 grams   21 oz
   Water   1 litre   1 gallon
   Nutrient content = 230 ppm nitrogen
   Used on cucumbers on straw bales for second three weeks after planting.

6. Potassium nitrate   25 grams   4 oz
   Ammonium nitrate   100 grams   16 oz
   Magnesium sulphate   25 grams   4 oz
   Water   1 litre   1 gallon
   Nutrient content = 191 ppm nitrogen: 58 ppm potash K_2O:25 ppm magnesium
   Nutrient ratio = $7.5N:2.5K_2O:1Mg$
   Used on cucumber on straw bales from six weeks after planting to end of season.

7. Potassium nitrate   72 grams $11\frac{1}{2}$ oz
   Ammonium nitrate   164 grams   26 oz
   Water   1 litre   1 gallon
   Nutrient content = 333 ppm nitrogen:166 ppm potash K_2O
   Nutrient ratio = $2N:1K_2O$
   Used as a liquid feed for vigorous pot plants with every watering. Used at half strength for slow-growing plants.

8. Ammonium nitrate   120 grams   19 oz
   Potassium sulphate   88 grams   14 oz
   Mono-ammonium phosphate   13 grams   2 oz
   Water   1 litre   1 gallon
   Nutrient content = 271 ppm nitrogen:30 ppm phosphate P_2O_5:203 ppm potash K_2O
   Nutrient ratio = $1.3N:0.15P_2O_5:1K_2O$
   Used for pot plants in peat-based loamless composts. 44 g (7 oz) of magnesium sulphate may be added.

Appendix III

Pesticides

1. 'Pesticide' is a general term which describes all chemicals used for the control of pests and diseases and for the destruction of weeds. Pesticides can be categorised according to their principal use, though relatively few have only one specific purpose. The following terms are in common use and in most cases their meaning is obvious:

Name	Pest controlled
acaricide	spider mites
aphicide	greenflies
bactericide	bacteria
fungicide	fungi
herbicide	weeds (herbicides have a sub-classification of their own)
insecticide	insects (including aphids)
moluscicide	slugs and snails
nematocide	nematodes (eelworms)
ovicide	eggs of insects and mites

2. It is usual to speak of controlling pests and diseases rather than curing or eradicating them. Control means limiting the incidence of the pathogen to an acceptable level. Nevertheless, it is often possible to prevent an attack from occurring, and sometimes possible to eradicate a pest from a crop for an extended period of time.

3. Almost all pesticides are freely available, but, for many, special precautions in their use must by law be observed under the appropriate regulations. Some compounds require full protective clothing to be worn by those using them, and others require a lesser but still high degree of protection for the user. These substances are taken out of effective reach of the amateur by the simple fact that they are not marketed in small enough packs to reach the garden centre and retail shop outlets. Some pesticides are scheduled as poisons and are, therefore, only obtainable on signature.

Although the amateur gardener will not normally be concerned with these regulations, you should, nevertheless, regard all pesticides with caution, and ensure that the instructions on the pack are observed to the letter. Manufacturers always give directions as to use, and the dilution rates they recommend have been established by intensive trial and investigation and must be adhered to. It is always dangerous to 'exceed the stated dose'.

4. Many pesticide chemicals fall into groups of related substances which tend to control the same categories of pests. The most important of these groups are:

The dithiocarbamate group These are fungicides used to control a wide range of fungal diseases including both downy and powdery mildews. Zineb, Maneb and Thiram are the best known and are used as protectant sprays. Thiram is also a valuable seed-dressing substance.

Copper fungicides These include the oldest effective fungicides we have, such as Bordeaux mixture (copper sulphate and calcium hydroxide), Burgundy mixture (copper sulphate and sodium carbonate), and Cheshunt compound (copper sulphate and ammonium carbonate). The two former are still used, although colloidal copper sprays have to some extent superseded them. Copper sprays are particularly useful against downy mildews and are used as protectants.

Sulphur and organo-sulphur compounds Sulphur on its own is no longer much used except for fumigating empty greenhouses. This is done by burning sulphur candles. Lime–sulphur has been used for many decades as a fungicide by the fruit grower. It is not, however, used under glass. The organo-sulphur materials are very useful modern safe fungicides. Captan is one of the better known.

Mercury compounds Mercuric oxide and mercurous chloride have been in use for a long time for seed dressing and for clubroot control in the cabbage family. Under glass, organo-mercury compounds were used for tomato mildew control and for other fungicidal purposes, but they have been superseded by new materials and will not be used by the amateur.

Systemic fungicides New fungicides within the last decade have been increasingly successful and further developments are likely. These are the systemic fungicides, of which benomyl is the best known. A systemic substance is one which is absorbed by the foliage or taken up by the roots of a plant and spreads throughout the whole organism.

The organo-chlorine group These were formerly called chlorinated hydrocarbons and include such well-known substances as DDT, BHC, aldrin and dieldrin. Because many are persistent chemicals and get into the food chains of birds and animals, their widespread field use is now restricted. Under glass the hazards to wildlife do not apply and smokes based on DDT and gamma BHC (Lindane) are still valuable insecticides and acaricides.

The organo-phosphorus group A very large number of these substances have been developed, mainly as acaricides and aphicides. They are mostly very poisonous. They include several systemic materials and are, unfortunately, substances to which aphids, red spider mites and white flies seem to develop resistance. Few are available to the amateur, but malathion is very valuable as an aphicide, acaricide and general insecticide under glass.

Carbamates These are mostly persistent chemicals used as wormkillers, nematocides and moluscicides but also as general insecticides. The only one likely to come the way of the amateur is the moluscicide draza; it is an excellent defence against slugs and snails.

Derris and pyrethrum These are plant derivatives which have for long been safe and reliable insecticides, particularly for the amateur. Active research and development is now directed towards the production of chemicals which have many of the properties of pyrethrum; these are called synthetic pyrethroids. They are expected to increase in number and to be approved for wide use as insecticides, particularly under glass. Resmethrin is the best known at the present time.

Appendix IV

Ventilation

---

1. Natural ventilation
Ventilation is the process whereby warm air within a greenhouse, because of its lower density, floats upwards and escapes into the external atmosphere through the overlaps of the glass and any other aperture.

In new, well-designed greenhouses, when the doors and ventilators are closed, this leakage of air brings about total replacement of the atmosphere within about two hours. In general, and especially in older houses, the rate will be about twice as fast, i.e. one complete change in one hour.

By providing ventilators along the ridge of the house the rate of air-change can be greatly increased, and if low-level side and end ventilators are provided also, the entry of external cooler air can be greatly facilitated by increasing what is called the 'chimney effect'.

2. Measurement of ventilation
The easiest way to think of ventilation is in terms of the number of air changes per hour (ac/h), but a more precise determination is to think in terms of air-flow.

If it is imagined that a fan, at one end of a greenhouse, were extracting air from within it, it is quite easy to picture the air flowing along and agree that this could be measured as the volume of air passing over a square metre (*square foot*) of floor-surface. It also follows that the taller the greenhouse, the greater the volume of air it would enclose and the faster this air would have to flow to bring about an air-change within the same compass of time as would be the case were it a lower house, enclosing less air.

The ventilation rate is thus stated as cubic metres of air per square metre of base area per hour (*cubic feet air/square foot/hour*).

3. Ventilation requirement
This cannot be stated precisely but there is general agreement that to provide efficient cooling in hot and still summer weather, air-flow rates of from 140–180m³/m² of base area/hour are needed (*450–600 cu ft/sq ft of base area/hour*).

The lower rate is appropriate for large houses, i.e. with an average height greater than 3 m

(*10 ft*), and the higher rate for small ones, i.e. with an average height less than 3 m (*10 ft*).

Flow-rates can be converted to air-changes per hour, by dividing flow-rate by average height. Thus for a garden greenhouse with an average height of 2.05 m (*6 ft 9 in*) the air-change rate would be (180/2.05) = 88 ac/h.

4. Ventilation provision

There is no formula for calculating ventilator provision from air-change rate.

Experience indicates that in larger houses, with side and end ventilators, effective cooling can be obtained with ridge ventilators providing an opening equal to 15 per cent of the base area of the house. Where there is no side or end ventilation the provision has to be doubled to 30 per cent of base area.

For garden-size greenhouses there is no stated recommendation but 30 per cent of base area with side and end ventilation is assumed to be adequate.

In practical terms this would mean that a garden greenhouse measuring 2.4 m × 3.7 m (*8 ft × 12 ft*) requires on both sides of its ridge 1.3 m² (*14½ sq ft*) of ventilator opening, which could be provided by ventilators on each side of the ridge, running its whole length and 0.36 m (*15 in*) wide (or deep).

To be effective these ventilators would need to open through 60° so that the opening provided is equal to the area of the ventilator.

5. Forced-draught or fan-ventilation

Positive ventilation can be provided by means of extractor-fans installed at one end, or side, of a greenhouse, with louvres at the other end, or side, which open, proportionately with the speed of the fan, to admit the replacement air. Fans and louvres are controlled by thermostats. The systems work effectively but are not really appropriate for amateur gardeners. The fans are noisy and the systems are dependent on an electricity supply which must be backed up by standby generators in case of power failure.

For further details see MAFF Bulletin No. 115, *Commercial Glasshouses*.

Appendix V

Soil sterilisation

1. As the temperature of the soil is raised there is a progressively more lethal effect upon its teeming population.

Thermal death points of soil organisms

Temperature °C	°F	Organisms killed or inactivated
55	130	All soft-bodied animals, e.g. earthworms, eelworms, slugs, protozoa; most weed seeds; nitrifying bacteria, and most plant viruses
63	145	Most of the fungi causing plant diseases, particularly root rots; all weed seeds
82	180	Fungal wilt diseases of plants, particularly *Verticillium* and *Fusarium*
88	190	Tomato mosaic virus (TMV) is inactivated.
100	212	Ammonifying bacteria form resistant spores and can survive quite long exposures
127	261	All living organisms

Lower temperatures for longer periods can have the same effect as higher ones for short periods, e.g. 43°C (*110°F*) for 10 minutes has the same effect as 63°C (*145°F*) for seconds.

2. The soil can only be heated effectively by causing steam to condense within it.
(a) It takes 112–118 g of steam to raise the temperature of 1 litre of dry soil to 100°C (*7–8 lb of steam per cu ft*).
(b) Dry soil can absorb steam at the rate of about 345 grams per litre per hour (*21 lb/cu ft/hr*); thus at this rate of injection, it takes about 20 minutes to bring the soil to 100°C (*212°F*).

3. The normal procedure of heat-sterilisation with steam is to raise the temperature of the

soil to boiling point (100°C/*212°F*) which is indicated by steam issuing from the soil surface. The soil being steamed is covered with a plastic sheet, which is weighed down around its edges. When this balloons-out with steam, the desired temperature will have been reached.

4. Amateurs sterilising small quantities of soil in steamers made from buckets or oil drums (see diagram) must allow one litre of water to about 7 litres of dry soil (*1 pint of water to 7 pints of soil*) and always add 25% more water to prevent the container boiling dry. A small sheet of plastic film must be tied over the top of the container. When this balloons, the container is removed from the heat source, or this is switched off and unplugged if an electric kettle or immersion heater is used to boil the water.

5. As heat 'sterilisation' does not bring about complete sterilisation, but allows the ammonifying bacteria to survive, the process is only one of partial sterilisation or 'pasteurisation'.

6. Chemical effects of heat sterilisation
a. The survival of the ammonifying bacteria and their subsequent rapid increase leads to higher levels of ammonia and ammonium compounds. These do not decrease until re-infection with nitrifying bacteria enables the ammonia to be converted to nitrate. The accumulation of ammonia is highest in soils containing a high level of organic matter, or those that are too moist, before steaming.
b. There is an increased availability of the major nutrients, phosphorus and potassium.
c. There is an increased availability of many minor and trace elements, but manganese is the only one likely to cause trouble. This is most likely if the pH of the loam was too low.

7. Physical effects of heat sterilisation
After heat sterilisation, loams have a somewhat higher field capacity (and thus container capacity).

8. After heat sterilisation to 100°C (*212°F*) soils and composts are very vulnerable to re-infection by pathogens, particularly fungal ones, because of their reduced biological competition. To compensate for this commercial horticulturists use lower temperatures – 66–71°C (*150–160°F*) – to pasteurise soil. This is accomplished by using mixtures of air and steam. The apparatus is sophisticated and beyond the reach of the amateur. This lower temperature is applied for 80 minutes and succeeds in destroying most fungal pathogens, but leaving many of their competitors alive. Re-infection is much slower in soils so treated.

9. Amateurs steaming their own loam for making composts should ensure that:
   It is dry.
   It has a pH in the range 6–6.5.
   Whenever a sample comes from a different source, it should be tested by sowing some antirrhinums which are highly sensitive to any toxic levels of ammonia or manganese.

Appendix VI

Soil conductivity

1. It is all too easy for excessive amounts of soluble salts to accumulate in greenhouse soils and growing-media. Originally chlorides, sulphates and nitrates were all thought to be involved, but now only nitrates are considered to be responsible in most cases.

2. As the concentration of soluble salts in a solution increases, its electrical resistance decreases, and thus provides a straightforward means of measuring this concentration.

3. For convenience the resistance of a standard soil solution is given as its arithmetic reciprocal, or conductance, which is 1/resistance (in ohms). The reciprocal of an ohm was formerly called a mho, but is now known as a siemens, and the conductance of a standard soil solution is expressed in micro-siemens. The standard solution is made by shaking air-dried sifted soil (below 2 mm grain size) with two-and-a-half times its own weight of a saturated solution of calcium sulphate, and its conductivity is measured with a Mullard conductivity bridge.

4. The Agricultural Development and Advisory Service of the MAFF has now produced a scale as follows:

Conductivity (micro-siemens)	ADAS Index
1900–2200	0
2210–2400	1
2410–2500	2
2510–2600	3
2610–2700	4
2710–2800	5
2810–3000	6
3010–3500	7
3510–4000	8
over 4010	9

5. Interpretation of ADAS Index

Light soils	Other soils (or light soils with high levels of organic matter)	
0	0	Normal range for outdoor soils.
0	1	Greenhouse soils with low nutrient levels.
1	2	Safe level for lettuces and flower crops.
2	3	Safe level for tomatoes.
3	4	Danger level for lettuces and chrysanthemums which will show restricted growth.
4	5	All crops likely to show some restriction of growth; and sensitive crops, seriously so.
5	6	Root damage and growth restriction on all crops.
6	7	Cropping impossible.

Drenching the soil with water will always lower the conductivity.

6. Earlier literature expresses conductivity on the pC scale, which was logarithmic and where a low numerical figure represented a high concentration, or on the CF scale where high figures represented high concentrations. Both are superseded by the ADAS Index.

Appendix VII

Micro-propagation

1. Micro-propagation has been developed from the long-established technique of botanical research called tissue culture. Some prefer to call it *in-vitro* propagation, and in view of the fact that it is a laboratory process and the propagules are kept in glass flasks, this is probably the best term. Micro-propagation, however, is the term which seems to be most popular.

2. Tissue culture was developed before the First World War by botanists, not with thoughts of propagation in mind, but for studying plant nutrition and many related processes. Small pieces of plant tissue are excised from the plant and usually placed on agar jelly, previously impregnated with a solution containing all the nutrients required by the tissue to continue its existence and to multiply. Kept thus, in completely sterile conditions, and provided the nutrients supplied are the right ones and in the right concentrations, the tissue can be kept alive almost indefinitely.

3. Micro-propagation developed from tissue culture when it was discovered that introducing hormones into the nutrient jelly could, in a reasonably controlled manner, cause excised meristems to multiply and form roots and thus new plants, which can be established in a normal environment.

4. As micro-propagation has developed it can now be seen to have three distinct functions to fulfil:
a. to provide a means of propagating plants vegetatively which are difficult to propagate by

other means. Epiphytic orchids, e.g. *Cymbidium*, provide a good example.

b. to provide a rapid multiplication method for plants otherwise intolerably slow, e.g. a new *Narcissus* cultivar would take, by natural multiplication, 16 years to provide 1000 bulbs, 6 to 7 years by the relatively new horticultural technique of twin-scales, but only 12 to 18 months by micro-propagation.

c. to establish new stocks of virus-free cultivars in plants normally propagated vegetatively and having severe virus problems, e.g. potato, strawberry, apple.

5. Micro-propagation is a sophisticated technique, requiring sterile laboratory facilities. It lies beyond the normal resources of amateurs and most nurserymen, though not necessarily all; but in view of its probable far-reaching consequences for the future, no apology is required for this brief description.

6. The tissue used as a source of propagules for micro-propagation may be:

a. Axillary meristems: These are the growth points found normally in plants in the axils of leaves (in buds) or at a more developed stage at the tips of shoots. The meristem is stripped of all its surrounding leaves until only the flat dome of the growing tip with two or three leaf primordia remain. This tip is then excised, probably under a dissecting microscope, to form the propagule, known in this case as an explant. The explant is sterilised and placed on a sterile nutrient base within a flask, where in due course it increases in size to form a small shoot. The hormone cytokinin is then introduced and causes the shoot to branch and form a cluster of shoots. If rooting hormone is then introduced, the shoots form roots and in due course the young plants can be established in a normal environment. Explants prepared in this fashion are known as meristem tips and are the kind used for attempting to raise virus-free stock, because whilst virus diseases are systemic and pervade the whole of the plant, the newly forming cells at the tip of the meristem are frequently not affected.

Shoots of *Callistemon citrinus* 'Splendens' (Crimson bottlebrush) in a sterile flask. The apical meristem has proliferated on a medium rich in cytokinin. It will soon be forming roots and will then be broken into single plants and carefully rehabilitated into a normal atmosphere.

Well-rooted shoots of
Callistemon citrinus
'Splendens' after growth
on a medium rich in
auxins.

Shoot-tip culture differs only from meristem-tip culture in that the growing point is not stripped of its leaves to quite the same extent and may be a few millimetres in length, even a centimetre, compared with the meristem tip which is only about 0.5 mm in length.

In the early days of micro-propagation shoot tips were often obtained from plants which had undergone 'heat therapy'. This was a process whereby the stock plant was placed in a very high temperature for several days before the shoot tips were excised. It was believed that the high temperature slowed down virus activity, but speeded the growth of the plant so that the shoot tips were growing faster than the virus could reach them. Little is now heard of heat therapy as this belief has proved to be almost certainly fallacious.

b. Adventitious shoots. Some plants do not produce axillary shoots at all, e.g. many palms, or else too few, e.g. *Narcissus* bulbs. In such cases it may be possible to use parts of plant organs, other than axillary meristems, in the hope that adventitious meristems will develop *in vitro* This is the case with the bases of the scale leaves of *Narcissus* bulbs, the leaf tips of orchids and small leaf sections of *Begonia* and *Streptocarpus*, all of which form explants capable of giving rise to adventitious meristems.

c. Callus. When pieces of plant organ are subjected to tissue culture, they often, if hormone levels are increased, give rise to masses of the undifferentiated tissues called callus. Callus can be multiplied and sub-cultured quite extensively and, in some cases, hormones can cause it to produce plantlets reliably. This is the case with *Freesia* and *Citrus*.

The possibility exists that callus when dispersed into minute, single-cell pieces to form a suspension in a liquid could be induced regularly to form thousands of plantlets.

7. Adventitious meristems to some extent and callus to a greater extent give rise to mutated plants or sports, most of which are aberrant and not worth keeping. However, this raises the possibility of a fourth function for micro-propagation; that of producing new cultivars.

8. Micro-propagation is a relatively new technique which will become more precise and certain as time goes by, and holds out exciting and far-reaching possibilities in many fields of horticulture and agriculture.

Further reading

Science and the Glasshouse, W. J. C. Lawrence, (Oliver & Boyd 1948)
Modern Potting Composts, A. C. Bunt, (George Allen & Unwin 1976)
Apricots, Peaches, Nectarines, Figs and Grapes, E. G. Gilbert, (Wisley Handbook 1972)
Seed and Potting Composts, W. J. C. Lawrence and J. Newell, (George Allen & Unwin 1946)

Glossary

Adventitious – botanical term for buds or roots forming in abnormal sites, e.g. buds on roots or roots on stems.

Air-filled porosity – the amount of air in a soil at field-capacity or a compost at container-capacity. Pore-spaces less than 50 microns in diameter cannot be emptied by gravity. Air-filled porosity is expressed as a percentage by volume. Compost in a container should have an air-filled porosity in excess of 15 per cent and evenly distributed.

Algae – green plants with a primitive organisation, without leaves or roots. Seaweeds are the largest, but freshwater forms are abundant. Algae form a green scum on permanently moist soil and other moist surfaces like that of a sand standing-down bed. Algicides are available.

Aluminium-alloy – aluminium is alloyed with various other metals for the purpose of increasing its strength without substantially reducing its weight or ability to be extruded. Exposed to the atmosphere it rapidly oxidises, with the resulting oxide forming a stable protective surface.

Ambient temperature – in horticultural terminology this refers to the temperature of the air in a greenhouse, frame or any enclosed space in which plants are growing.

Ammonification – the conversion by bacteria of organic nitrogen into ammonia and ammonium salts (mainly ammonium carbonate). See *nitrification* and *mineralisation*.

Angle of incidence – the angle at which light-rays strike a surface. It is taken as the angle between the ray and a line perpendicular to the surface the light is striking.

Apical dominance – the power that a terminal shoot has of suppressing the laterals on the stem below it. It is a hormonal response, and when the leading tip is removed the hormone is shared by the shoots below it. One of these often ultimately acquires dominance.

Artificial irradiation – the practice of submitting plants to electric light in order to
a. supplement or replace natural light to bring about increased photosynthesis, or
b. increase day-length to bring about a photoperiodic response.

Assimilates – these are sugars and starches (carbohydrates) manufactured in the leaves of plants through photosynthesis or carbon assimilation and stored in various organs, e.g. tubers, nodes.

Base-material – a horticultural term for the material of which a *standing-down bed* is made.

Biodegradable – the susceptibility of organic matter to decay through the agency of micro-organisms.

Botrytis – a name by which the ubiquitous grey mould fungus (*Botrytis cinerea*) is universally known by gardeners. It is sometimes a facultative parasite passing from dead tissue into living, e.g. on the stems of tomatoes, or establishing itself as a primary parasite, e.g. ghost spots on tomato fruits.

Calcicole – a plant tolerant of chalky soils. See *pH*.

Calcifuge – a plant tolerant of acid soils and highly intolerant of chalky soils. See *pH*.

Chimney-effect – convection currents in the atmosphere within a building whereby warmed air, which is less dense, rises to the top of the building and escapes through apertures such as chimneys or ventilators, and is replaced by cool air entering from outside.

Chitting – the germinating of seeds before actual sowing, usually on moist sand, moist cloth or in specially prepared gels; also the sprouting of tubers (such as potatoes), before planting.

Cleat – now any of a variety of fasteners, e.g. clips holding wires, pipes etc; blocks of wood acting as stops to prevent panes of glass slipping, as in a Dutch-light.

Compost – a mixture of materials. In horticulture it may mean a mixture prepared for the growing of plants in containers, or a mixture of decomposing or decomposed organic materials of animal and vegetable origin. In the former sense the term 'medium' is gradually replacing 'compost' in the U.K., and has replaced it in American and Commonwealth usage.

Conduction (of heat) – the flow of heat through a substance by the transmission of the increased movement (energy status) of its atoms.

Container-capacity – comparable with *field-capacity* in that it represents the equilibrium between the retentive power of the compost in the container and gravity. It varies with the depth of the compost, its air-filled porosity and the base-material on which the container is standing. The moisture tension is normally lower than the average value for field-capacity.

Convection – the transport of heat through liquids and gases in currents caused by changes in density, e.g. warm air rising and escaping through the glass-overlaps in a greenhouse.

Cordon – in its horticultural sense, any plant pruned and trained in such a manner as to be restricted to a single stem (literally: a cord), e.g. vines, tomatoes, cucumbers.

Cotyledon – a seedleaf. Cotyledons are part of the embryo plant contained within the seed. In most seeds these appear above the soil and function as green leaves. If damaged, the growth of the seedling is inhibited.

Damping-down – the process of spraying with water all the surfaces in a greenhouse. It was formerly practised with the intention of cooling the atmosphere, increasing its relative humidity and discouraging red-spider mite. It is now known not to succeed in any of these.

Diffused light – light reflected and diffracted from the particles of the atmosphere and the various solid and liquid surfaces of the earth.

Electrolytic corrosion – this occurs in greenhouses when galvanised steel is in contact with another metal. In the presence of moisture an electromotive force is generated, causing a current to flow between the metals. This removes the zinc from the steel, thus exposing the steel to rusting.

Epiphyte – a plant which grows on another plant in a non-parasitic fashion. It merely lodges itself upon its host, but makes no other demands upon it. Epiphytes are common in tropical rain-forests; orchids are the best-known examples.

Evaporative cooling – the heat energy used in changing the state of a liquid to that of a gas (latent heat of evaporation). Plants dissipate about 40 per cent of the heat they absorb from the sun in transpiring water from their leaves, thus maintaining a constant temperature.

Eyes – dormant buds.

Facultative parasite – a *saprophyte* which possesses the ability in certain circumstances to become a *parasite*.

Fertilisation – in flowering plants this follows successful pollination. The pollen grain germinates, and the pollen-tube grows down the style into the ovary of the flower. When this tube locates an ovule where the female gamete is located, the male gamete passes into the ovule and unites with the female gamete. From this union the seed develops.

Field-capacity – the amount of water held by soil against the force of gravity after it has been saturated and all subsequent drainage has ceased. The water in the soil at field-capacity is held at a tension of around 0.5 bar (sometimes expressed logarithmically as pF 2.7). See also *container-capacity*.

Field factor – the proportion of viable seeds which through various causes fail after germination to become established seedlings. It is expressed as a decimal fraction, e.g. 0.25.

Frit – soft glass ground to a fine powder which contains trace elements. The one known as FTE 253A contains boron, copper, iron, manganese, molybdenum and zinc. Added to plant-container composts, particularly loamless ones, the trace elements are made available to plants in a slow-release fashion.

Galvanised steel – mild steel which has been electroplated with zinc as a protection against rusting.

Greenhouse – any kind of growing house, including plastic structures. The term 'glasshouse' is restricted specifically to glass-clad structures as distinct from plastic ones.

Greenhouse effect – the heat gain within a glasshouse due to incoming solar radiation penetrating glass more readily than outgoing radiation from the earth's surface.

Hormones – growth-regulating chemicals produced within the plant, which control and organise its growth and development. Their existence was suspected by Darwin in 1880, but the first to be isolated was auxin (3-indolacetic acid) in 1931. This and other hormones may be synthesised, as may chemical analogues with similar effects.

Incident light – the direct radiant light from the sun.

Integral light – the total light energy arriving at a given point, comprising both incident and diffused light.

Irrigation harness – the arrangement of irrigation pipes, tubes and nozzles in a greenhouse attached to one water source.

Keiserite – a form of magnesium sulphate ($MgSO_4.H_2O$) containing less water than Epsom Salts ($MgSO_4.7H_2O$) and used as a fertilizer for greenhouse soils. It is not recommended for inclusion in composts.

Lateral – a sideshoot developing from a main stem; also called a break.

Light-transmission – the amount of light which can be passed through a transparent or translucent material such as glass or plastic film.

Lime-induced chlorosis – see *pH*.

Limiting factors – a term used by botanists and horticulturists to describe environmental factors which limit the rate of *photosynthesis*. They are: light intensity, temperature, CO_2 concentration, and the availability of water.

Loam – theoretically, a soil in which the mineral constituents (sand, silt and clay) are present in such balanced quantities that the characteristics of none prevail. In practice such soils are extremely rare, and a whole series of terms is in use (sandy loams, silty loams, clayey loams, heavy loams etc) in an attempt to define precisely the texture of soils within the medium range.

Low-temperature corrosion – the attacking of metal surfaces in chimneys, flues and boilers by sulphuric acid. Sulphur dioxide and water in flue gases combine to form sulphurous acid which oxidises to sulphuric acid, which condenses at about 32°C (*90°F*). It can irreparably damage solid-fuel boilers, the temperatures of which are allowed to fall in periods of low heat demand.

Medium, or **growing-medium** – see *compost*.

Mineralisation – the conversion by bacteria of organic matter into inorganic matter. It is mainly used by horticulturists in connection with the conversion of organic nitrogen into nitrate. See *ammonification* and *nitrification*.

Minimum night-temperature – the lowest temperature to which the atmosphere of a greenhouse is allowed to fall. Night is specified because there is no help then from solar radiation and everything relies on the heating system. Modern growers now speak of night and day temperature settings.

Moisture deficit – the amount of water a soil has lost from field- (or container-) capacity. It is usually expressed in millimetres of water. Crops in greenhouses are usually grown in soil which is brought back to capacity as soon as it has acquired a deficit of 13 mm (*0.5 in*).

Mono-cropping – the practice of growing the same crop repeatedly on the same site.

Mulch – normally a covering applied to the surface of the soil. The covering might be:
   a. an organic material, e.g. peat, farmyard manure, leaves;
   b. plastic film (floating mulch);
   c. gravel or rock chippings;
   d. a tilth of dry soil (dust mulch).
All mulches suppress weeds, but their other effects are more difficult to evaluate.

Mutation – a genetic change giving rise to a plant with some new or changed characteristic. Most mutations are undesirable, but some are capable of exploitation by the gardener. The changes are inherited by subsequent generations.

Nitrification – the conversion of organic ammonia or ammonium salts into nitrate, commonly calcium nitrate. The process is both micro-biological and chemical. See *organic nitrogen* and *ammonification*.

Node – the swollen area on stems where buds and leaves arise. The node often contains a reserve of *assimilates*.

Organic nitrogen – the nitrogen in chemical combination in the tissues of the plant: an essential component of proteins and thus of protoplasm.

Orientation – the alignment of a building relative to the cardinal points of the compass. It originally meant alignment to the east.

Parasite – a life-form which gains its sustenance by feeding on another organism.

Parthenocarpy – the ability of some plants to form swollen seedless fruits without fertilisation. Greenhouse cucumbers constitute the most familiar example, but others exist, e.g. seedless grapes.

Pasteurisation – a process devised by the great French bacteriologist Louis Pasteur and named after him. It is normally brought about by the controlled heating of a material in order to destroy selectively some of its microbial contents, e.g. partial steam-sterilisation of soil, which does not destroy ammonifying bacteria.

Peach-case – a simple lean-to greenhouse built against a wall to protect fruit trees trained in fan-fashion against the wall. It normally has no roof-section.

Pelleted seed – any seed surrounded by a pill of inert material to make it larger in size, so that it can be sown singly by means of a precision-seeder. The belief that the 'pill' contains fertilisers is erroneous. The uses of pelleted seed in amateur gardening are so limited that the extra cost of the seed can rarely be justified.

pH – a measure of the acidity of a solution, defined as minus the logarithm (to base 10) of the hydrogen-ion concentration:

$$pH = -\log (H^+)$$

On the pH scale, $pH = 7$ represents a neutral solution (or pure water); solutions with pH less than 7 are acidic, and those with pH more than 7 are alkaline. A pH difference of one represents a difference of ten times the hydrogen-ion concentration.

Most crop plants have an optimum pH of around 6.5 in mineral soils, but it can be much lower in organic ones. At low pH values aluminium and manganese salts become increasingly soluble, poisoning the plants, whereas at high pH values their insolubility causes a deficiency of these elements which leads to a characteristic yellowing of the leaves called lime-induced chlorosis.

Phosphate – phosphorus is applied to the soil as calcium phosphate in either its water-soluble forms (superphosphate and triple superphosphate) or its water-insoluble forms (mineral phosphate and basic slag). Bones in the form of bonemeal or steamed boneflour are sources of very slow-release phosphate, too slow for horticultural purposes under glass. The phosphorus content of a fertiliser is expressed in terms of its oxide equivalent (P_2O_5) and it must be stated by the manufacturer whether this is water-soluble or not.

$$P_2O_5 \times 0.436 = P \qquad P \times 2.291 = P_2O_5.$$

Photodegradable – a photodegradable substance is one liable to chemical change brought about by light-energy. In horticulture it mainly refers to plastic materials, particularly plastic film.

Photosynthesis – the ability possessed by green plants to fix atmospheric carbon by utilising light energy. Some botanists prefer to call it carbon assimilation.

Pinching (pinching-out or stopping) – the act of removing the growing point of a shoot.

Point-watering – an irrigation arrangement whereby each plant container has its own individual watering point.

Pollination – the transfer of pollen from the anther to the stigma. If, as is usual, the pollen is transferred to the stigma of a flower on a different plant, it is cross-pollination; if to the stigma of the same flower or a flower on the same plant, it is self-pollination.

Potash – the term used by the fertilizer industry to describe fertilizers containing potassium ions (K^+). Potassium is normally supplied to the soil in the form of either potassium sulphate (K_2SO_4), potassium chloride (KCl) or potassium nitrate (KNO_3). These are equivalent to 48 per cent, 60 per cent and 46 per cent of potash (K_2O) respectively.

$$K_2O \times 0.830 = K \qquad K \times 1.205 = K_2O$$

Prilled – a fertilizer prepared by the shot-tower process, whereby it is dropped in a molten condition so that it breaks into discrete particles like lead-shot. Prilled fertilizers have the advantage of being very easy to scatter.

Radiation – the direct transmission of heat from an energy source through space to matter which absorbs it.

Relative humidity – the amount of water-vapour held in the atmosphere, expressed as a percentage of saturation. As the atmosphere becomes less or more dense with the rise or fall of its temperature, the amount of water it can hold decreases or increases. Thus relative humidity depends on temperature.

Renewal pruning – any system of regular pruning which seeks to replace wood that has flowered and/or fruited with new wood for the next season's crop. Renewal systems tend to maintain trees and bushes in a steady state.

Rooming-out – the spacing out of containers to prevent overcrowding and the 'drawing' of the plants. Plant pots when touching are said to be pot-thick. Plants when pot-thick may be **a.** on the square, i.e. their centres are at the corners of a square, or **b.** staggered, i.e. their centres are at the corners of a rhombus.

Root-death – this occurs to the roots of plants when they are killed without the activity of any pathogen. An absence of oxygen and accumulation of CO_2 is a common cause in circumstances where air-filled porosity in a compost is too low.

Root zone – a term referring to the zone in which the roots of plants in containers or in hydroponic systems are located. Warming of the root-zone is advantageous for cucumbers.

Rubbing-out – refers specifically to the removal of laterals, when they are young and soft and easily removed by hand.

Saprophyte – a life-form which gains its sustenance wholly from dead plant matter.

Seed – may refer to the tubers of potatoes – an unfortunate and confusing use of the word.

Seed-viability – the percentage of seeds capable of germination.

Selfing – see *pollination*.

Sets – pieces of rootstock divided by cutting to form propagules, e.g. rhubarb, or alternatively tubers or rhizomes planted to raise new crops – e.g. potatoes, Jerusalem artichokes.

Sideshooting – see *rubbing-out*.

Slow-release fertilizers – these are fertilizers in which the nutrient(s) contained have to undergo some process of chemical change before they are available to plants. This applies to organic materials like hoof-and-horn meal, and to the specially prepared compound fertilizers the granules of which may be resin-coated.

Soil-conditioner – a term frequently applied to peat and to other humified organic matter which, when mixed with the soil, improves its aeration and increases its moisture-holding capacity.

Solar radiation – the total energy received at the earth's surface from the sun.

Span-roof – a roof having the shape of an inverted 'V', i.e. with two sloping sides spanning the distance between the eaves and the ridge. A building with only one sloping roof, from a wall which functions as a ridge, is called a lean-to or (confusingly) a single-span.

Sport – a term describing aberrant growth on a plant arising *de novo*. It usually arises in one cell, or in a small group of cells. There are various causes, but many sports are highly prized and are propagated vegetatively. See *mutation*.

Standing-down bed – a horticultural term for any specially prepared bed of sand, peat, gravel etc. on which plants in containers are stood.

Thermal dormancy – a condition found in a number of annual and biennial seeds. It is a device to prevent germination occurring when temperatures are too high, when conditions are unlikely to be conducive to the proper development of the plant. Seeds of butterhead cultivars of lettuce and Japanese cultivars of onions display this characteristic.

Turgidity, or **turgor** – the state of the living cells of plants when they are full of sap and fully distended. If plants lose moisture by transpiration faster than their roots can absorb it, their cells lose turgidity, becoming flaccid. This causes wilting.

Vernalisation – the process whereby a plant achieves 'ripeness to flower'. It can be induced in many plants by the effects of temperature, e.g. flower-bulbs.

Vinery – on the island of Guernsey any kind of greenhouse, but on the British mainland, a span-roofed glasshouse of width 8.5 m (*28 ft*).

Winter-wash – an ovicidal spray applied to deciduous woody plants when they are dormant.

Index

Page numbers in *italics* indicate the sites of major discussions. For reasons of space, not every species is individually indexed; however, every genus discussed *is* indexed so that readers looking for a particular species should consult the pages listed after the appearance of its generic name.